D1500099

Straightjacket Barbie and Other Stories
A Collection of Short Fiction and Poetry

David H. Reinarz

ISBN: 9798697773819
Imprint: Independently published

Other Books by David H Reinarz

Exit Signs: A Collection of Short Stories, 2019

Is That A Short Story In Your Pocket, Or Are You Just
Happy To See Me? (A Bunch of Short Stories), 2019

They Might Be Poems, 2020

CONTENTS

DEDICATION

This book is dedicated to Lynne, the love of my life and my muse, and to the members of the 7 Doctors Writing Workshop Alumni Group (Greg, Grace, Jennifer, Michelle, Stephanie, Rick, Steve, John, and Teresa).

Thanks to the numerous friends and family who have read and commented on these stories. Your contributions have been greatly appreciated.

DISCLAIMER

All the stories in this book are works of fiction.

None of the people or events depicted are real, nor are they based on real people or events.

The descriptions of some places may remind the reader of actual places, but the content of the stories has no intention to factually replicate anything real in any place.

All the stories in this collection were written in 2018-20.

Very Short Stories
(start with a pair of homonyms or homophones)

I said, "Je t'adore."
She fingered a button on her blouse as she said, "Shut the door!"

•

The ferry tossed upon the choppy current
as the steely-eyed woman in the food service galley
tried to spread currant jam on a stale bagel.

•

Mourning has broken me
Like the first morning I awoke
and felt the depth and breadth
of your absence.
The mourning dove does not bring
the olive branch of peace.
The mourning dove brings a mouthful of ashes.
The morning of my discontent wreaks havoc
on my heart.
Your side of the bed reeks
with the fading scent of you.
Is a donut whole
if it has a hole in its center?
What about me
now that you're gone?
How is it
that you seem so full of yourself
without me?
Bist du ein Berliner?

•

In this cloister,
we are not allowed

9

to read aloud,
but the books they give us to read
are nothing you would want to hear.

                    .

"Now that we live in this Putin-esque dystopia,"
I whine,
"I wonder if we will ever be permitted to travel to Italy
and dine on wine and Puttanesca in the Roman twilight."

                    .

Everybody, including me, hoped you were the one, wanted so
badly for you to be the one. Friends don't want friends to be
lonely, to be alone. I don't want to be lonely. I like sharing
my life with another person.

It seemed to start out well, we got along, did things together.
People said what a nice couple we were. People said they
thought you really liked me. You weren't allergic to dog
dander, and I switched to vegan. I slept over at your place
after the concert. You went camping with me in tents in the
National Forest.

Dave, the bartender, refills my glass and says, "So why are
you talking about her in the past tense?"

                    .

Although Jackson managed to get Georgina to the altar,
it didn't alter her feelings for Fritz.

                    .

I lay bare
on the bear skin rug.
Is it too much to bear
that I am no longer a child
and there are no longer any secrets left

10

for my soul to bare?

•

I didn't inhale.

As my face turned blue
and I nearly passed out,
I coughed and blew the smoke in her face.
She inhaled my second-hand smoke.
She didn't blink.
She just said,
"Maybe we can get past this,
But you have to let Monica go."

•

The plasterer was in the process of sealing
the cracks in the ceiling
as Michelangelo fretted
over his frescoes.

•

He threw caution to the wind
and exited through the bathroom window.

•

"What do we not share, mon cher?"
she queried in her uniquely queer way,
dangling one shoe on the tip of her toe.
I weighed a response.
"I know no thing large or small."
I stated in my staid way.
"I see you're being literal," she said,
"and I'm being litoral,
as I wait for you on the edge of a sea of love."

"Hear me clearly, ma cheri," I replied,
"I am already here in the water, doing the backstroke."
"Ahh! There you are, mon petite chou!" she giggled
as she kicked off her other shoe and dove in.

•

"We thought we were safe, on hiatus,"
said the Oreos stashed under the couch,
"but the guy who was high ate us."

•

Let's say you know he's lying.
He lays the lies down,
scatters them about
like the wilting flower petals
from ten thousand dismembered leis.
You know there is no truth in it,
and yet here you are
gathering it all in,
pretending you are unaware
that he's the con and you're the mark.
You want him to look into your eyes
and tell you another one.
You don't care that it's false.
How good was it for you anyway
before he came along?
How much worse could it be for you
when he leaves?
Rode hard, put up wet,
raped and left for dead in a ditch
at the side of the road?
You wanted it to be great,
and, for a moment, you believed it was.

•

I was shoveling chow into my face,
eating like there was no tomorrow,
not really paying much attention
to anything except what was on my plate.
Having worked all night at the whiskey barrel factory,
I was starving.
She said, "Ciao, baby!" as she slipped away
into the dim light of early morning
on her way to the one room schoolhouse
where she taught the Three R's
to a bunch of surly, ungrateful kids.
I grunted my farewell.
Maybe she would have liked a kiss.
She used to like a kiss now and then.
Maybe I would have liked a kiss,
but you can't eat a kiss.
I shrugged and looked at the fridge,
thinking there might be a hunk of cold meat in there.

•

I wondered if this was one of those sects
where you were expected to have sex
with the guru.
I looked around at the other faces in the room.
Yeah, they would probably have sex with the guru,
desperate for a little affection to go with their enlightenment.
Was being judgmental one of the things I would have to give
up?
I was going to leave
right after the ridiculously vapid and incoherent
welcoming speech
by the seminar coordinator,
a really intriguing looking woman
who was a Wall St. broker
until the guru showed her the light,
or whatever it was he showed her.

But there were those cookies,
like the ones they give you when you check into the hotel,
and the Kool-aid was really delicious.

•

On his deathbed
Buffalo Bob felt it was his duty
to tell the world
that Howdy Doody was not a real boy.
"What?" "What?" stuttered the assembled journalists.
Bob with great effort raised himself up onto his elbows and told them
"Indeed! Howdy Doody was a dummy,
a puppet, a marionette,
and his voice was actually my voice
altered to sound like a kid's."

There was stunned silence.
"I know the illusion was so seamless," Bob said, "so masterful,
that it was easy for you to be drawn in and come to believe he was real.
We all wanted this delightful boy to be real,
like the perfect son, the best friend you could have."

One of the reporters patted Buffalo Bob on the head
and said, "We knew that. Everybody knew that. I mean, it was a TV show."
Another reporter said, "Nobody thought Howdy Doody was human, Bob."

Buffalo Bob shook his head
and collapsed back into his pillow,
And with his last breath muttered,
"Never mind."

●

I sprinkled some Penzey's Tsardust Memories
on a split butternut squash
and slid it into the oven to roast.
Then I poured myself a cold dose of Slivovits,
put Nat King Cole's recording of Stardust on the turntable,
plopped into my favorite arm chair and pored over
Remembrance of Things Past.
I passed out,
dreamed of Nadia, sweet Nadia, fragrant and fleshy Nadia.
I awoke. It wasn't Nadia.
It was my squash beckoning me to arise
and devour it.

●

The plane descends into
The Plain of Jars.
I am soloing this time,
piloting a rugged and reliable Pilatus PC-12,
the perfect craft for open field maneuvers
requiring short takeoffs and landings.
So unlike the last time I was in the area,
back in the 60's,
our B-52's flight path over this remote place,
we dumped our load,
200 million explosions.

Now 80 million unexploded bombs
litter the field that I approach.
It will take a century to find them all,
if anyone has the will to do it.
If I can land in one piece,
I can find a moment of peace
among the burial urns of an Iron Age civilization,
an enduring relic of life
back before Nam when we lived in caves,

when we cremated our dead
instead of the living.

Cowboy Hedgehog
Prompt from Natalya Reinarz-Muller

You probably never saw
A hedgehog on a horse before.

We are not indigenous to North America.
We have been brought here
Against our will from across the big water.
We are kept in cages for the entertainment
Of homo sapiens.

Yet, here I am
Out of my cage
Riding a horse,
My little hands and feet gripping
The horse's mane tightly.
I ride high up on his head
so I can whisper to him.
One growl for right,
Two squeaks for left.

Bobby Joe can't be out here
On the horse.
He's cooped up inside
With the cough and the fever.
Irony.
He's in the cage
And I am out.

Moms can't ride a horse
With that bad hip.
Haven't seen Pops for weeks.
He may be gone for good.
The cattle have to be moved
To the north pasture.

Who else is going to do it?
Yippie kie yay.
Cowboy Hedeghog.

While I'm out here on the prairie,
I'll find some sassafras and red willow bark and baby
snakeskins
To make a healing tea for Bobby Joe.

Even if he gets better
I'm not going back in the cage.
Once you've smelled sagebrush
and sweaty horse hair
and felt the evening breeze in your quills,
You can't ever be fenced in.

Yippie kie yay!

Bukowski: Self-portrait in Quadriptych(A Parody)

1.Bukowski Goes to WalMart

The woman checking me out
at the discount chain store told me the total.
I handed her a wad of crumpled up bills and some loose
change.
It was the exact amount.
She looked at it.
She looked at me.
She counted it.
Twice.
"Have a nice day," she said.

I thought there was something in the quality of her voice,
a tone.
Or maybe I was looking for a hint of judgment.
"Have a nice day. Really?" I replied evenly.
"Like, maybe I was having a not so nice day,
and you needed to recommend
an attitude adjustment?
Does my breath smell bad?
Does my scruffy unshaven face suggest despair?
Does my unkempt thrift store wardrobe hint at a life in
shambles?"

She just looked at me.
Completely non-plussed.
Like she gets this kind of rant from people all the time.

"Thanks," I said, escalating.
"I WILL have a nice day.
I was going to go home
and close myself up
in the tiny dark coat closet

in my tiny dark bachelor apartment
and drink this bottle of cheap vodka
I just bought
until I passed out.
But now I won't,
because YOU told me to have a nice day.

Instead,
I'm leaving here
and I'm going to the Humane Society,
and I'm going to adopt an abused and abandoned dog,
and I'm going to take him to the park
and play Frisbee with him
until we're both so tired that we want to puke.
And then the dog and I
are going to my tiny dark bachelor apartment,
and we are going to order in pizza,
and we are going to eat it on the floor together,
and we are going to watch TV
until we fall asleep in each other's arms.
And I will dream of me and my ex-girlfriend,
Hillary,
laughing and playing Frisbee in the park that one day
until we were so tired that we wanted to puke.
And in the morning,
when I wake up in a pile of pizza bones
and a puddle of dog pee,
and my pee,
I will remember that Hillary left me
for the Highway Patrol cop who wrote her a speeding ticket
that day six months ago
when she slammed the door on her way out
of our tiny bright sunshiny couple's apartment.
And then I will take the dog back to the Humane Society,
because I can't really take care of a dog properly,
or a girlfriend properly,
or even myself properly.

And then I will come back to this God forsaken WalMart,
and I will buy TWO bottles of cheap vodka,
and, as you are checking me out,
I will tell YOU to have a nice day,
because SOMEBODY ought to have a nice day,
and I obviously don't know how to have a nice day.
I know how to sit alone in a tiny dark closet
in a tiny dark bachelor apartment
with two bottles of cheap vodka
and fantasize about lost love."

She didn't flinch.
She just looked me straight in the eye,
handed my the receipt,
and firmly replied,
"See you tomorrow, then, Loverboy."

2.Bukowski Goes on a Date with a Vampire

What was I doing in a fancy cocktail lounge
amongst all these glittery people
and all these glittery drinks?
Not that I was against drinking…
Drinking was one of the wobbly and continuously
decomposing cornerstones of my life.
It was the glitter that was disconcerting.
But being somewhat disconcerted is to be expected
when you are so lost you end up on the right side of the
tracks.
Of course if your pockets are empty of glitter
and it's not the guys from the aircraft factory buying rounds
for the house,
how do you get drunk in a high class place like this?

Throw yourself on the mercy of the bartender.
Not your average retired ancient mariner here.
A lovely lass with skin like milk glass
and double dimples when she smiled.
She smiled when she asked,
"What's a guy like you doing in a nice place like this?"
I professed that I once was lost but now was found.
She hoped I was possessed of an embarrassment of riches.
I proffered that I was too self-absorbed to be embarrassed
but also not rich.
I offered to trade a poem for a libation.
She mixed me a Cosmopolitan but held it in abeyance.
I hit her with:
"Roses are red
Violets are blue
That drink really sucks
But I'm liking you."

"That's not poetry. That's doggerel," she said.
"My dog could do better. Try harder."

I hit her with:
"Rivet rivet rivet
Bombs over Tokyo
It's no joke you know
When your ass gets fried by American nukes
But peace ensues
So sue me"

She handed me my drink
and charged it to some sucker's tab.
We hit it off.
My poetry.
Her motion.
I mixed metaphors.
She mixed aquifers of alcohol.
At closing time, all the fancy drunks went home.

I fancied following her home.
She didn't demur.

"Why don't you shave while I slip into something more
comfortable," she said.
"I don't usually shave," I said.
I thought shaving was a conceit of the aristocracy.
I thought scruff was rough and tumble,
as was I.
"I didn't bring my overnight bag," I said. "This was all so
spur of the moment."
"Don't be coy," She said. "It doesn't suit your persona.
There's a razor somewhere in the bathroom."

I found a used and abused blade on the edge of the tub.
I envisioned her shaving her legs and who knew what else.
I scraped away at my stubble.
I nicked my Adam's apple.

My cursing summoned her to my aid.
She found the rubbing alcohol and a cotton ball
and dabbed it on the wound.
She tilted her head and looked at the gash.
She licked it,
then licked it again.
She said, "Maybe there's a cocktail in there somewhere."

"I love it when you say cocktail," I quipped.

Three in the morning.
A jagged crust of blood on his neck.
She laid her tongue against it.
The moisture and heat dissolved it into a metallic bitterness
enhanced by the residue of alcohol.
She thought of gin and tomato juice
and something just out of reach of her brain.

I stirred. She shook.
"If you're gonna keep us up all night doing this," I mumbled,
"I'm gonna need a beer."
She kept it up. No beer. Something else.

Time marched on.
Still awake, she bit him deeper.
It was so much sweeter when there was an open wound.
"Leave some for me," I prayed.

How much blood could she take from him
to keep him in a state of weakened torpor,
suspended animation,
without killing him?

She splashed a little vodka onto her bloody lips,
Salt and pepper.
Where did she put the celery?
She had another before heading out to work the night shift.

I half woke,
Staggered stuporous down the stairs and sat on the curb.
Looking for the Number 2 Downtown.
Dozed on the bus,
rode it to the wrong side of the tracks,
to the end of the line.
My regular bar was at the end of the line.
It was called The End of The Line.

The average retired ancient mariner who owned the place
looked at me with a jaundiced eye.
"You look worse than usual, Loverboy," he croaked.
"I was waylaid by the Pale Horsewoman of the Apocalypse,"
I said.

"It was a bad day in Black Rock and an even darker night," I said.
"What'll it be?" he said, "You need to replenish some nutrients."
"What the heck," I said. "Gimme a Bloody Mary for my soul and a raw steak for my neck."

3.Bukowski Falls Down the Stairs

I probably fractured a hip
In this slip and fall
Down the stairs at the end of the hall

Not so bad I can't walk
But it hurts like a mofo
And there's going to be a huge ugly bruise

A bruise to match the one
On my face where the guy who lives in the apartment
At the end of the hall
Hit me because I tried to wrestle his pint of Jack
Away from him because he wouldn't willingly share

Note to self:
In future even if you're involuntarily sober and hung over
And need a little sumpin' sumpin' to get the day going
Don't wrestle with a bigger guy
Who's already drunk this morning.
I think this at the bottom of the stairs
Bruised and broken.

But when you're broke and payday is days away
And you have to get to the aircraft factory
To work out the month and get your pay envelope
And there is no money for doctors or a bottle of brown

You have to limp back up the stairs
And knock on the neighbor's door
And try again to get his bottle
Because all you need is a sip or two to take the edge off
The pain so you can get to work
You understand what it was really like
For those Cro-Magnon guys who lived or died hunting
With their hands and centuries later we dig them up
And look at their bones
And wonder how that caveman broke his hip and his jaw
I can tell you it wasn't that sabre-tooth tiger that got him
It was the guy in the next cave
Who wouldn't share his fermented honey

Those flyboys who keep America safe
And guarantee my freedom
Need my hungover broken drunk again ass
Down at the aircraft factory
To rivet together the planes they have to fly
So back up the stairs I go
Here comes America's greatest generation
Loverboy
I say to myself as I knock knock knock on heaven's door

4.Bukowski Is Given a Piece of His Own Mind

(Re-imagining "Wax Job" by Charles Bukowski)

"You got a cigarette?" I said
to the lady sitting on the barstool

next to the one on which I had just plopped down.
I always use the term "lady" loosely, considering the "ladies"
who normally populate my world,
but this lady was clearly drinking below her pay grade here.
She looked at the cigarette in her hand, looked at me,
then blew a sarcastic stream of smoke
through her flared nostrils.

"Ok," I said, "a different cigarette from the one you're
currently smoking
for a no longer secret admirer of yours."
Her upper lip curled
as she handed me the one from her mouth.
The filter tip tasted like expensive lipstick dipped in a
campfire.
"Those things will kill you," she said as she lit up again.
"Nah," I said, "my liver will get me first."
She looked at me long and hard.
I could see she was an empath.
"I'll race you," she said.
I waved over the bartender and ordered whiskey,
one for her and one for me,
and we were off.

"So what do you do in life," she said,
"when you're not drowning whatever in a dive bar
or getting rolled by deviant college kids in an alley
or dealing with another case of the crabs?"
"I rebel," I said, "against the expected norms of the military
industrial complex.
I mourn the lost souls crushed by a culture of shameless
greed and corruption.
I jump off the merry go round of the rat race.
I rage against the machine literarily
and literally through my bohemian lifestyle"

She laughed.

"We all ride the machine, darling.
The machine makes the cigarette you're smoking.
The machine makes the booze you're drinking.
The machine makes the flop house you live in.
The machine makes the typewriter on which you bang out
your poems.
The machine makes the backhoe that digs the grave they
dump you in when you die."

"The machine is a raging bull,' I protest,
"And I'm a rodeo clown."

"Loverboy," she said,
"Right now you ride the machine like a wild mustang,
headlong for the edge,
not even sure if you will fly when you leap off the cliff
or plummet to the canyon floor."

"Luckily my thrills are cheap!" I quipped.

"Tomorrow," she said, "when you make a few bucks from
your writing
and move to a little house with a white picket fence in the
'burbs
and marry a good woman,
you will still be riding the machine.
You'll just be riding it like an old lady
in the backseat of a chauffeured limo,
not even considering that you will run out of gas
on the plains of the Serengeti and be mauled by lions."

I ordered another round.
I considered what she said.
The whiskey tasted like the smoke
from the crematorium down the block.
"Nah," I said, "my liver will get me first."

Four Poems for Spring

1.Spring

The babies come in the spring.

The robins have babies.
The rabbits have babies.
You have a baby.

You look at the baby,
and the baby looks healthy.

The baby looks healthy
when it is awake and active.

The baby looks healthy and alert
and looks around and gurgles
and plays with its toes.

But who knows if the baby is really healthy
or only seems healthy
to the ignorant eyes of a new parent?

And now it is night
and the baby must sleep
and you must sleep.
The robins are asleep.
The rabbits are asleep.
Shouldn't the robins be awake?
There are cats out at night.
Shouldn't the rabbits be awake?
There is surely a fox hunting.
Shouldn't you be awake?
Is the baby still breathing?

Is there some death dealing pathogen lurking in the
environment?
Will the baby get tangled in the blanket and suffocate?
Why is the baby sniffling and coughing?
You are watching.
You are watching so closely
that the abandoned game of solitaire
closes its window on your phone.
Fine.
You will need your phone to call 911.

2.Warm enough

It is warm enough to be outside.

It is warm enough to be outside
without a jacket.

It is warm enough to be outside
in the short-sleeved unbuttoned plaid shirt
my mother made for me
in the winter just past.

It is warm enough to be outside
barefooted
in the woods that surround our neighborhood
and lie under this pine tree
on the soft bed of last fall's fallen needles.

It is warm enough to be outside
and play hide and go seek
and hide so well that my brother passes by and doesn't see
me,
and the kid with the always green teeth who lives up the
street runs by and doesn't see me.

It is warm enough to be outside
and fall asleep under the pine tree
unfound
on the soft bed of needles
and dream of never being found
until the snow falls,
and under the snow
the soft blanket of the coming fall's fallen needles
covers me
and keeps me warm enough inside.

3.Melt

I always get excited when spring is near
and winter's accumulated snow,
now soiled with pollution,
starts to melt.
Really melt.
All the way down to the ground.

Then I can see the popping up
of all the delightful things
that have been hiding under that dirty blanket
since last fall.

Baby grasses.
Beer cans.
Daffodils.
Discarded condoms.
Sidewalks and bus stops.
Those little single dose peppermint schnapps bottles.
And there are buds on the trees.
And there are grease stained hamburger wrappers.
And there are birds singing.

And there are disposable syringes.
And the whole world is waking up
to the realization that it has transitioned
from being the big blue marble
to being our great gray wastebasket.

Dedicated to Cyndonna Tefft.

4. The Poem You Can Always Get Published in Nebraska

A red winged blackbird sits on the fencepost
at the edge of the yard
in front of the old farmhouse.

This plain brown and gray woman of a bird
reminds me of my grandmother.

The wind ruffles her feathers
as she looks out across the cornfield
toward the abandoned tractor
and chirps and screeches for my grandfather
who is not there.

Nefarious Nursery Rhymes

1.Play Misty

One misty, moisty morning
when cloudy was the weather,
Jill met an old man
All dressed in leather.
Well, not old old, not ancient,
but he was older than she was.
She liked an older man,
an older man like Georgie Porgie,
even though he was plump as a pudding.
Maybe it was the leather
and the cigarettes and the hip flask.
Maybe it was the motorcycle.
Maybe it was the way he kissed her.
The way he kissed her made her cry...
in a good way.

Jill went up the hill
carrying the pail
with which she and Jack
got water from the old well.
Jack was still asleep
when she snuck out.
She groused about the hill.
Why didn't this godforsaken town
dig the well in the dell
like everywhere else?
But it was a secluded spot
early in the morning
in the mist,
before everyone else was up,
a good spot to meet a man
in leather on a motorcycle.

Jack was not asleep
when Jill left the house.
He was only feigning sleep
even to the point of fake snoring.
He knew when Jill was up and about,
even if she was being stealthy,
sensed it,
that being a natural thing between twins,
that and the sense of responsibility
he felt ever since their parents died so tragically
on that hill, going for water
on a misty, moisty morn,
just like today,
then slipping and falling on the wet grass,
tumbling down down down,
breaking their crowns,
then getting infection from that old quack of a doctor
who plastered their skulls with vinegar and brown paper.
Now Jack had to be the man of the house.
Jack didn't understand his sister's need to sneak off,
his twin sense meeting its limitations.
He asked her once, begged her to stop.
She only said,
"Jackie, boy, a girl's entitled to a little adventure
every once in a while."

Jack sat in the corner of the kitchen and brooded.
Should he go after her?
He wanted a piece of pie.
He wanted a drink of water.
He noticed that the pail they took to the well
was missing.
It was all well and good to be the black sheep of the family,
but going up the hill on a misty, moisty morning,
well that was too much!
He put on his boots
and was out the door.

Georgie Porgie didn't mind the mist
and the pre-dawn grayness.
A pretty girl was on her way to meet him,
and he thought that a little damp weather
was nothing in the grand scheme of things,
the grand scheme being kissing girls
then riding away on his motorcycle
as they cried for more.
And what a motorcycle it was!
A right cock-horse this one was,
the kind of cruelly beautiful machine
that made girls weak in the knees
and other men envious.
This Jill who was coming up the hill
was a right lovely girl
with fire in her eye
and a willingness to give as good as she got.
He imagined that they would kiss
and otherwise fool around for a bit
then ride his cock-horse to Banbury Cross
where they would stop in at the coffee shop
that he knew she liked
and have one of those skinny lattes.
Before he saw her, he heard her coming,
rings on her fingers and bells on her toes
making an eerie and seductive music
in the morning mist.
Georgie Porgie shivered.
Would this Jill be the one to make HIM cry?

Jack was running now.
He shouldn't have given Jill such a head start.
He was scrambling and starting to backslide
on the slippery slope.
He could hear a motorcycle engine roar to life.
"Damn you, Georgie Porgie!" he shouted.

"Damn you to Hell!"
Jack's feet lost their purchase
and his arms flailed ineffectually.
He tilted like a windmill with a rotten foundation.
He apologized to his dead parents
as his head hit the turf.

Georgie Porgie thought Jill
was slipping her hand into his pocket
for prurient reasons,
but, alas, the lass was fishing for his keys.
He was glad it was raining.
If anyone else had seen him crying
as the girl kissed him and then rode away on his motorcycle,
he would have never lived it down.

Jill shifted into high gear.
She could already taste
the lovely skinny latte on her lips,
maybe a hot cross bun, too.
Adventure!

2.Humpty

Humpty Dumpty sat on a wall,
even though the wall had a warning sign posted:
This is a square wall!
The top is narrow and square.
The sides are square and vertical.
People with hard round asses will roll off and fall!
If you are round or ovoid, don't sit on the wall!

Humpty scoffed!
He had worked hard to maintain
his hard, round ass,
hours and hours at the gym,

protein shakes, stair-climber
pumping iron,
sweating to the oldies,
unlike those other guys
who thought golf and beers was a workout.
He would scale the wall, sign be damned,
And gaze upon the other side.

Humpty didn't like other people telling him what to do.
Maybe he was an egg,
but he wasn't a baby egg.
He was a grown man egg!
There was a great view of Mexico
from the top of the wall.
Humpty liked looking at Mexico.
He thought of Mexico as exotic and scenic
(and dangerous, ergo the wall).
He wouldn't ever go there,
but if he wanted to look at Mexico,
who was going to stop him?

Humpty got a ladder from the back of his monster truck.
He climbed and climbed,
then he sat on the wall.
He was a little tipsy,
a little rollie polie,
as he settled his hard, round ass on the parapet,
but the view was spectacular!
There were verdant fields
of peppers and onions and tomatoes
and avocado orchards,
and beyond the fields and orchards
there were mountains.

Were those innocent hard working farm laborers
or drug cartel soldiers?

He leaned forward to get a better look.
He should have brought binoculars.
An ill wind blew from the north,
and Humpty wavered and wobbled,
then had a great fall.
Down, down, down!
Oh, the humanity!
He cracked his cosmic egg and spilled his guts.

Nobody came to his rescue.
Nobody tried to put Humpty together again.
What kind of round ass white boy gringo would sit on that
wall?
Didn't they have signs to discourage stupid behavior?
They shrugged their shoulders.
He was nobody to them.

3.Shoe

There was an old woman
who lived in a shoe.
Yeah, a shoe.
Not a metaphor.
You can't live in a metaphor.
OK, not a SHOE shoe like you would wear on your foot.
You can't live in an actual shoe.
It was big, really big, as big as a small house.
It was the last hole at the miniature golf course,
the one where your ball goes away
when you putt it into the cup.
A big old shoe.
Abandoned like so many other things during the pandemic.

The kids all came home with fevers,

that little house on the prairie they called home,
last house on the left at the end of the lane
where it petered off into the forest,
whitewashed picket fence and all.
It seemed like she had been continuously pregnant
for decades.
That's what you get living in an anti-science misogynistic
authoritarian patriarchy.
Her sister was dead,
so she had her sister's five kids plus the twelve of her own.
Bunk beds wedged into every available nook and cranny.
Her husband was dead.
Drank himself into a wet brain coma a year ago,
visions of wolves and dragons and spiders
dancing in his head.

The schools had opened
before the virus was done with humanity.
Packed classrooms, no masks,
nationwide hand sanitizer shortage.
Her seventeen kids with fevers.
Little Tommy hacking up half a lung.
What do you do with so many sick kids?
She didn't know what to do.
She gave them broth without any bread for dinner
and put them to bed.
She was soundly whipped.
They were all gone in the morning.
The Pied Piper of community transmission had taken them.

How was she not dead?
How would she go on living after all that
with who knows what waiting for her?
Get away. Just get away.
She had a cot and a sleeping bag
and a couple pairs of sweats.

Boots. Winter coat. Guitar.
She threw stuff in the van and drove until she ran out of gas.

The van rolled to a stop
in front of Fairy Tale Farms Pumpkin Patch and Golf.
She walked around the place until she felt at home.
Humpty Dumpty had a hole,
so did Hansel and Gretl, Peter Peter, Jack and Jill.
There were bathrooms in the clubhouse,
a souvenir shop and a snack bar.
She could last a while,
if she rationed her intake of popcorn and candy bars.

How old was she, really?
Forty something?
She broke off a piece of a Kit Kat bar
and practiced her putting stroke.
Not bad for an old woman!
Her ball went into the giant old shoe.
She opened the door next to the heel.
She went in.
In the cool darkness,
she laid herself down and went to sleep.
She didn't know what else to do.

4.Foster

Doctor Foster always wanted to be near a toilet.
This had been the case
since he was a boy.
In his boyhood
he had several embarrassing "accidents"
which caused him to be hypersensitive and hyperalert.
He could not remember ever sleeping straight through an
entire night.

Once on a school field trip to Gloucester,
a shower of rain fell on the children
parading to the National Waterways Museum.
Water water everywhere,
there was nothing he could do.
Alas!
To hide his shame
he stepped into a puddle up to his middle.
He never went on a trip like that again.

His life was tightly circumscribed.
He knew the location of every bathroom
WC
Loo
Outhouse
Restroom
Powder room
Locker room
in a five mile radius of his home and work.
The lovely town in which he lived
had wonderful little shops
up and down the High Street.
His work was conveniently across the street
from his home.

Doctor Foster was not a medical doctor.
Perhaps he might have been,
but there was too much unpredictability
in a medical doctor's life.
What does one do if one is up to one's elbows
in someone's thoracic cavity,
and one desperately has to pee?

Doctor Foster had wanted to be a private detective.
He read detective fiction voraciously
as a kid.
He usually had the crime solved by chapter two

and ruthlessly criticised the gumshoe
for his lack of perspicacity and insight.
I can do this, he thought.
But then there was the tailing of suspects
and the all night stakeouts
and the lying unconscious in the warehouse after a gratuitous
beating.
He would surely piss himself.
The pretty but mysterious person of interest
would surely pass on someone like that.

So he became a librarian.
Reginald Foster, Ph.D. L.I.S
Every library had books to read, lots of books.
And bathrooms. Multiple bathrooms.
Doctor Foster even had a private executive restroom
next to his office.
The library, his library, in his town in the Cotswolds
was renowned for having the most thoughtfully curated
crime and mystery collection in Europe
and the cleanest bathrooms in the British Isles.
School children on field trips
paraded in the rain to marvel at it all.
Doctor Foster smiled benevolently at them
from his office window
then grabbed a Raymond Chandler anthology from his desk
and quick-stepped to the crapper.

5.Q

Q did,
in fact,
have a counting house
in which she counted all her money.
It was her money, now that K was dead.
He had succumbed to the virus,
having comorbid conditions,

including but not limited to COPD and obesity.
There was a lot of money.

It took her a significant amount of time
each day
to count it.
The counting house
was on the estate
where she lived,
perched on the edge of a cliff
overlooking the western ocean.

After Q counted the money,
she would evaluate her position
vis a vis the micro and macro-economies
and make adjustments,
because, when she came back the next day,
she wanted the number that was the total of all her money
to be bigger.

Q was educated,
unencumbered by spouse or children or elderly parents,
living in a liberal state
in 21st century America.
As long as the money held out,
Q thought she was untouchable.
Q wanted to be untouchable.

Q would take a moment now and then
amid the counting
to rest and stretch.
She would gaze out the window
at the waves crashing on the rocks,
the surf foaming as it ran up and down the beach.

Today, the blackbirds were swirling,
a great storm of birds.

These were not cute, happy songbirds.
They were a malevolent tornado
of wings and talons and beaks.

M was back at the big house,
having just finished the laundry,
she was hanging it on the line in the courtyard.
The cloud of birds moved in that direction.
Q had watched all the Hitchcock movies.
She knew this was not a good sign.
She picked up the phone and called the house.

C answered the phone.
She was in the kitchen.
By the time she got to the courtyard,
M was down.
The birds were on her,
in a feeding frenzy.
They weren't even cowed by the appearance of a human in
their killing field.
C grabbed bed sheets and threw them over M.
She swung her kitchen knife like a Saracen warrior.
Blood and feathers and flesh commingled at her feet.

M lost her nose and one eye in the fracas.
When she was released from the hospital
and returned to the estate,
Q and C and M celebrated with a feast.
The main course was four and twenty blackbirds baked in a
pie.
When the pie was opened,
the women sang a song,
a song that told a story,
not of untouchability,
but of survival and vengeance.

Life in the Age of Plague)

**My Dog is a Little Ho(a)rse
(or Spillover 2020**

My dog is a little hoarse.
This morning, his bark is more like a cough...
keh, keh, keh.
He looks at me as he languishes in his doggy bed,
as if he once thought I was so smart, but now he's not so
sure.
Keh, keh, keh, rufff
That rufff was a little rough.

He's a big dog.
People often ask,
"Is that a dog or a little horse?"
He's so big that you might think he's invulnerable.
He never needs a trip to the vet,
healthy as a horse, that one.

Certified trained service animal,
so he can travel with me, which I like.
I get anxious when I fly, and he calms me down.
It's worth it, paying for an extra seat on the plane.
And those guys who sell bracelets outside the Sacre Coeur
don't mess with me.
Mon Dieu! Le petit cheval! Ha!
Keh, keh, keh, rufff, yip.

Love this dog!
Traveled the world with him.
Great companion.

Not a picky eater.
Calm and adventurous all at the same time.

But now I'm thinking,
keh, keh, keh, ruffffffffff, yip, pant pant pant,
maybe it wasn't the smartest move to share
that freshly butchered pangolin
in the wet meat market in Wuhan this past Christmas.
It seemed like the thing to do at the time.

He loves it when I rub his tummy.
I love it when he gives me sloppy kisses.

Keh, keh, keh.
This dry cough is annoying.
Where did I put that humidifier?

(From covid quarantine, 2020)

Out of work

"social distancing"
"sheltering in place"
"lockdown"

I'm self-employed.
I am in what you might call the direct wealth acquisition
and redistribution business.
Maybe you don't think about guys like me
being out of work.
I gotta be next to you,
bump into you,
jostle you a little.
No crowds in Times Square,
no crowds in museums,
no crowds at concerts and sporting events,
no crowds on buses or the subway,
no bars over serving their clients.
I mean,
what's a person to do
when your income is dependent on
being up close with people?
Now that I can't get close to you,
I am out of work.

I have some reserves,
but rent and food are expensive in the city.
I keep some cash
stashed in my apartment,
but I really need some drivers license and credit card
and insurance info to sell on the dark web.

I can't even get a $1200 stimulus check
I don't pay taxes.

The IRS doesn't even know who I am or where to find me.
I don't want them to know.
Anyway, who thinks $1200 will last more than a week?

Maybe I'm not Robin Hood,
but I am working hard to help
cycle money through the economy.
Circulation is key to making capitalism work.
Some people want to hoard and sequester assets.
I break down their walls,
get into their pockets,
spread the wealth out more equitably.

Yeah, maybe you don't feel so sorry for me.
Maybe you don't even want my marketplace to reopen,
but you sure want your marketplace open.
That's cool.
Su casa, mi casa.
I'll wear a mask.
I'm a team player.
Let's get this economy back up and running.

(From covid quarantine, 2020)

Pandemic Love

I didn't know I was in love.
I was asymptomatic for days.

That little catch in the throat,

The flip flop of the stomach,

Loss of breath,

The fever,

My body's on fire!

It will not go away like some miracle,
Like the fall chill taking away the allergens,
Like the snow melting in the spring.
Maybe I don't want it to go away.
I am a long haul trucker for love.
I need intensive care.

(From covid quarantine, 2020)

We Are Food

We are food.
We don't think of ourselves as food.
We think of ourselves as
The Crown of Creation,
The Masters of the Universe,
The Peak of the Pyramid,
The Tip of the Iceberg,
The Top of the Food Chain.
We are the eaters, not the eaten.

But we ARE eaten.
The Earth is full of things that eat us now,
Or will soon eat us.

Bacteria, viruses, and other microbes
Are in us, right now, chewing away.
Mosquitoes, lice, ticks,
Parasitic worms, leeches don't just lurk,
They seek us out, hunt us, prey on us.

And, if we are not fortunate enough
To live in a First World neighborhood,
There are the rats, the wild dogs,
The lions and tigers and bears (oh my),
The sharks. The sharks!

And watching and waiting for us to fall,
The carrion eaters, the scavengers,
The vultures, the hyenas,
The beetles, the flies,
The worms,
The microorganisms that turn us back into dirt.
Dust to dust.
What ho! You angels in the outfield!
Your imaginary teleology bumps into

The circle of life.
Laugh while you can, Monkey Boy!
What bones are left will be the new fossils.

(From covid quarantine, 2020)

Spent Flower

I am a spent flower.
I have been too long in this place,
too little sunshine and fresh air
and dirt and rain.

My petals fall from my face,
brown edged and wilted,
a drift of tattered snow
where my roots once were.

My scent is cloying decay,
appropriate perhaps for this funereal existence,
but not my formerly fresh style.

I no longer stand up straight,
my stem a-droop.
I am undone!

She smiles upon my wastrel state,
lifts me from my thirsted vase,
gathers up my mortal remains,
and places me between two sheets of waxed paper
into her favorite book of poetry.

"You are so beautiful,"
she says,
as she puts me under her pillow
and goes to sleep with me.

(From covid quarantine, 2020)

Anxiety

The anxiety is sneaky.
It doesn't need a proximate cause
Or a precipitating incident.
You can be having a perfectly delightful day,
And then the sadness is there,
And the fuzzy-headedness is there,
And the weakness is there,
And the feeling of imminent doom is there,
And the hopelessness is there.
Chemicals are released into your body.
Physical changes occur.

There is this thing in you
That isn't you,
But it is you.
It must be you because it doesn't go away
And you don't believe in demonic possession.
It must be you,
Even though you are normal and happy and optimistic
And your life is free of things to dread.
You are one of the lucky ones.
It lies dormant for long periods of time,
And you think you are shut of it,
Then one day it is there again,
"Hello, Darkness.."

Of course, there are kids you know whose parents leave one
day
And never come back.
Of course, there are people you know who get brain tumors
and have heart attacks
Even though they seemed perfectly healthy.
Of course, there are people whose spouses leave them,
And people who inexplicably become drug addicts,
And people who die in horrific automobile crashes,

And people who get fired from their jobs and end up
homeless,
And people who inadvertently catch the novel corona virus
and, unable to breathe, die alone,
And people who get neglected and abused by people who
should care for them,
Etcetera, etcetera, etcetera.

None of these people is you.
You have glided through life
Relatively unscathed,
And yet you see the possibility of scathing.
Lurking.

After you lie down and have a cup of tea with honey,
And think to yourself that this is just anxiety,
You have to let it go,
Let it go.
Maybe the fog lifts,
Maybe the sun comes out,
Maybe the anxiety goes back under its rock,
The rock that is in the back corner of your consciousness.
And you sleep.
And you wake up unanxious.
And you walk about in the world.
But the anxiety is not asleep.
It is only under its rock
Lurking.

(From covid quarantine, 2020.)

Viral Vocabulary
(Wordplay with Seventh Grade Vocabulary)

Opportunities for infection Abound.
The virus is a Braggart.
It lives in her, an evil Cache.
How to fight it needs much Clarification.
I am Despondent.
The hidden enemy our happiness will Embezzle.
She sends me away to safety Heartrending.
Death lurks Leisurely.
She becomes Lethargic
With this Malady.
How can I be Mellow?
Split off, I become Nomadic.
Unity of purpose fractures into desperate Piecemeal.
Without one's love, what can be a worthy Quest?
Life casts slings and arrows Random.
Against the coming night I Rant.
I cannot hold her hand to Reinforce.

(From covid quarantine, 2020)

Viral Vocabulary Part Deux
(Word play with seventh grade vocabulary)

It was not a nervous or anxious Agitation
That caused my love to Blurt,
Nor was it appropriate in a Chronological
Sense at this early hour to Diminish
Caution and allow you to Enchant
Me, nor did my heart Fluctuate
In its desire to Foster
Deeper connection, so I did Grovel
On my knees, my protestation of affection a rude Handicraft,
Which you found Hilarious,
Though I hoped it might Ignite
A fire of great Magnitude
In you, a Massive
Miscalculation. Your pity of me, near Maternal,
Cast a Pall
Upon my Reputable
Attempt to express how much I Revere
You. It makes a tragic Saga
That, until you see me as I see you, our intercourse will
remain Stodgy.

(From covid quarantine, 2020)

1984

I was wrong about 1984.
Not the book. The book has nothing to do with it. Well,
maybe a little. I read 1984 in high school.
The time I was wrong about 1984, the year, was just after
high school. I was in college. It was 1969 or 70. I had been
reading a lot of eco-disaster literature, fiction and non-fiction.
I told several of my friends that there would be this massive
crashing ecological wipeout of the human population in 1984.
It was inevitable. The woman I was dating said, OK, maybe
in Africa or India or Brazil, but not America. We have
grocery stores and air-conditioning and cars, so we'll be OK.
I said that's the stuff that's causing the eco-disaster. She said
have a breath mint and kiss me. I did, and I momentarily
stopped thinking about the eco-apocalypse. Then I noticed
that she didn't have her eyes closed. While she was kissing
me, she was looking past my shoulder. I disengaged and
turned. There was a guy sitting at the next table in the college
library. He was reading Architectural Digest. She would
probably be dating him next week. He would tell her about all
the money to be made in upscale suburban development as
they drove in his air-conditioned car to the grocery store.

There was a lot of messed up ecological stuff in 1984. The
sixth major die-off of species was well underway.
Desertification in Africa. Chopping down the Brazilian
rainforest. Pollution in India. We just hadn't gotten to the
part with the massive human death toll.

Now it is 2020. The Covid-19 pandemic is raging. Global
warming is frying the planet. The polar ice is melting. Oceans
are rising. Democracy is in retreat. There are 8 billion humans
burning and pillaging the earth. The extinction of humans by
their own hand does not seem crazy at all.

The thing is, once we got past 1984, I thought I might outlive the humans beating the lemmings to the cliff dive into oblivion. Now I'm not so sure. I may well be swept up in the conflagration. There is disease out there waiting for me to break quarantine. International supply lines for goods are disrupted. The heat is making it hard for the tomatoes in my garden to set fruit. Secret police are kidnapping people off the street in Portland.

I think all this while sitting in my air-conditioned car waiting for my turn to go into the suburban grocery store where they may or may not have toilet paper. I pop a breath mint and wonder if it will ever be OK again to kiss a woman in the library.

(From covid quarantine, 2020)

Rain

"It's raining in the cloud," I write.

No matter how bright the moon,
if it is obscured by a bank of clouds,
it is dark in my cell.
It's tricky to write in the dark
on scraps of paper gleaned from the trash
with the stub of a pencil
and be able to read what you've just written.

Just impressions,
thought into words,
I impress onto something flat and not necessarily blank.
Am I confident
that the inscription will adequately express my thoughts,
that my thoughts will mean anything to me later,
when I tuck this shard of mental pottery
into the seventh archeological layer of the shoebox under my
bed?

Tonight there is a cloud
in the process of eclipsing the moon.
Good to have a cloud, especially one of the tall fluffy ones.
They have been rare.

It's not raining here,
on the ground.

It's too hot.
The water vapor can form droplets higher up in the air
but the droplets can't merge into bigger drops
with sufficient mass
to attract the attention of gravity.

It should be snowing up here in The Hills.
It's November
but it's not snowing.

When I get up and
go outside into the dark,
early morning,
the coolest part of the day,
I walk barefoot across the sparse dry grass,
tufts in parched dirt.
Everything out here smells like dry dirt.

Back inside,
I write,
"The moonlight on dusty brown mat fades."

We are in the florid stage
of this global dis-ease.
This part of the earth is no longer covered with flowers.
Being red in the face,
if you've been outside even for a little while in the day,
is no longer remarkable.
Can I still write beautiful verbally complex sentences?

I write, "I keep my hair cut short."

Is it cold outside?
Anywhere?

I lie down and close my eyes and feel the heat penetrating my
body.

There is no more space left for writing.

I dream.
A pregnant woman.
Astride a horse.

We had all agreed,
come to the unexpressed conclusion,
that we are just playing out the string, treading water, until we
all die.
There is not even the half-hearted sense of obligation to sire
children,
to reproduce and continue the species.
We have been thinking to ourselves that we are the last of the
homo sapiens.
Now, there comes to me this vision of soon to be born child.

I open my eyes.
Who would dare?

(From covid quarantine, 2020)

Reflections Pursuant to a Spiked Watermelon Brought to the Church Picnic by the Man with a Hat and Suspenders Whose Wife was Called Felicity (A Parody)

(Re-imagining "Reflections on a Gift of Watermelon Pickle
Received from a Friend Called Felicity" by John Tobias)

During that summer
when unicorns and other myths and fairy tales
fell down and skinned their knees
on the roughly paved sidewalk of reality,
a fat green frog of a watermelon
was gigged with a switchblade knife
and force fed a quart of moonshine from a Mason jar
at the church picnic
by the man with a hat and suspenders.

During that summer,
I thought about Felicity,
daily,
watched Felicity,
pretty Felicity who ought to benefit
from the softening effects of civilization
but didn't,
because civilization does not soften men with hats and
suspenders
and switchblade knives and moonshine
and watermelons.

After the prayer and the fried chicken
and the green bean casserole and the Jello salad,
the man with a hat and the suspenders
sliced the watermelon with his switchblade knife,
thick dripping slices,
and passed them to the other men.
They sucked and slurped and spit seeds and made crude
jokes,

and one of them lit up his liquored fruit with a Zippo and ate
it flaming,
and the women watched and tut-tutted,
except Felicity who turned her back and walked away.

That summer now seems far in the past,
but the past lingers,
haunts in tiny bites here and there,
conjuring up the sight of her straight back and purposeful
stride
and the look in the eye of the man with a hat and suspenders.

Once a year,
in summertime,
I open a quart jar of watermelon pickles
and eat a few
and leave the rest,
a gift,
on her grave.

That Thing...(Twelve Easy Pieces)

1.That thing that happened to you, and you know people are
always saying "if it doesn't kill you, it makes you stronger,"
and it didn't kill you, not totally kill you, but it was close. You
thought you were going to die. There was this moment when
you thought you were dead. Well, you're not stronger, not
even a little bit stronger. You have zero strength. You can
barely pull the covers over your head. You may never get out
of bed again. You may never eat, never sleep, never walk,
never talk. Then your mother sticks her head in the door and
yells at you, "Cut the crap, Cynthia, it's just a boy. There are
more boys." You roll over and hide under the pillow. If you
were stronger, like in the proverb, you would get up and kill
your mother, then find that boy and kill him. But you're not,
so you lie there and wish for sleep.

2.That thing when you're opening a package and you're in a
hurry, because you really want what's in the package, and you
know you should put on gloves and get that knife that is
good for opening packages, because you always get a paper
cut when you use your bare hands, but you're in a hurry, and
you really really want what's in the
package...SONOFABITCH.

3.That thing when you are pretty sure you know how to do
the math, equalize the sides of the equation and solve for X,
but then they give you this word problem about a girl named
Sheila and her startup soap company and all the ingredients
she uses to make soap, and it's in metric quantities, and
you're never ever going to work in a soap factory and
probably never use algebra again, so you think, "Screw Sheila
and her stupid soap," and you close the book and go back to
playing video games.

4. That thing when you get elected secretary-treasurer of the student council when you should be president, but Donny got president only because he's quarterback on the football team, and he's not even a good quarterback (his INT to TD ratio is shit and the team hasn't won a game in two years), and Charlie got vice-president (why? I mean he's Charlie for godsakes), and Judy is events coordinator only because she's the girl everyone wants to get with. OK, so here's how it's going down: I have the checkbook, and they are NOT spending the money from the cheerleader bikini car wash fundraiser on a fucking pizza party. I am writing the check to the homeless shelter right now.

5. That thing when the kid's blanket reeks of perfume and is covered in cat hair. OK, nobody likes it that we split up and the kid has to go back and forth between my house and her house. The kid has this blanket that he always wants with him. Maybe it's a continuity piece, something constant in his world turned upside down. I always wash it before he goes to her place, so it's clean, sanitary, fresh, none of my cooties on it. When it comes back with him, it's like her cats have been nesting in it, and it smells like that perfume she used to wear when she cruised the bars, that she wore the night she picked me up and took me home with her, that she stopped wearing after we were married, that maybe she's not so subtly telling me she's wearing again. OK, I get it, but I won't rise to the bait. I won't confront her and argue. That's over for me, the confrontations, the arguing. I'll just wash it on the inbound and the outbound. De nada.

6. That thing when Google and Facebook keep showing you ads for the Alfa Romeo Giulia sport sedan, and you look at it for a few seconds, and you say, "Huh!" So they show it to you again, but you don't really want an Alfa Romeo, you don't even want a car, more good mass transit would be nice. Well, maybe one of those all electric cars would be OK for the environment. And then they show you the red one, and it's very much like the red one you rented in Europe and

really enjoyed driving around Southern France, and maybe that's how they know you might want one, the red one, the color of red that is the color of the freshly spilled blood of Italian racing car drivers as they are horribly decapitated because they were driving too fast and launched off the road into a tree, and your blood starts to flow more excitedly in your body. So you turn off the computer and take a cold shower. But later you check the evening news, and the local dealer inventory is available online, and there are twenty two Alfa Romeo Giulia sport sedans in your town, and one of them is red, and it has the sunroof and the eleven speaker premium sound system and the eighteen inch alloy wheels, and the dealer wants you to come in for an espresso and a test ride, but you don't really want a car, but what would it hurt to drive one...

7. That thing when you've made toast for breakfast, and it's perfectly golden brown, and it's perfectly hot, and you reach for the butter to spread on the perfect toast, and (horrors!) there is no soft, easily spreadable butter on the butter dish. You stand there with the knife in your hand, staring at the empty butter dish, realizing there is only cold, hard butter still in the wrapper in the fridge. Putting a chunk of cold hard butter on your now cooling perfect toast is not an option, so you reach for the soft, creamy peanut butter. This is not your first choice. You don't like peanut butter when it's hot. Something weird happens to the taste. You almost put the toast down and go back to bed, but then your dead mother's voice is conjured up, and she reminds you that children in China are starving. So… peanut butter toast it is.

8. That thing when you think it's a drop of blood, and all kinds of wild, crazy, scary ideas run through your brain like a scattering herd of cattle being chased by a pack of wolves. But it's not a drop of blood and a few feet away another. It is a red sequin from her Santa hat and a few feet away another, and another down the hall toward the bedroom, and all kinds

of wild and crazy Merry Christmas celebration ideas run through your brain like a family of rabbits set loose in Mr. MacGregor's garden. And then you hear Bossa Nova Holiday Music playing in the bedroom, and you remember that's your mother's favorite album, and you realize that this is your parents' apartment, not yours, and you came over to surprise them, and you must have arrived just before your father got home from work. And then your mother calls out, "Is that you Herbie? Hurry up, baby cakes!" And you tiptoe back down the hall and quietly let yourself out and pray that's not your father coming up on the elevator.

9.That thing when you are in college, and there is a big Physiology and Anatomy exam tomorrow, and you should be studying the digestive system, but instead you are at this party, and you have had two glasses of Mateus Rose', and the guy who is hosting has this killer stereo system with the biggest sub-woofer you have ever seen, and it's pumping out this amazing Euro-techno-dance music, and Bibi, the girl from Sweden who is in America studying Liberation Theology and its Relationship to Situation Ethics, is sitting on the couch all by herself with her head tilted back and her eyes closed and her mouth partly open, and when you sit down next to her she says, "Can you feel that bass line in the music driving itself into the core of your being?", and you think to yourself, "This is the appropriate way to study physiology and anatomy."

10.That thing when you've been into it for a while, really deep into it. I'm talking dark web shit and secret meetings and doxing liberal college professors and safe houses and pseudonyms and semi-automatic weapons training. And then there's the really pathetic and frankly weird sex stuff. And even though you're upgrading from the flat out Neo-Nazi guys, you wonder...is there really an upside to being a white supremacist fan girl?

11.That thing when you're the local campaign field worker for that Green New Deal candidate and tonight's meet and greet in the absolutely critical Midwestern swing state is a meat raffle at a biker bar.

12.That thing when you know thousands of people are going to die if you don't do something, but the cheeseburgers are on the way, and you have to order more orange fake suntan cream from Amazon (fucking Bezos) before Jerry Junior and his wife get here (damn she's hot).

Fundulus kansae
(A Villanelle)
Epigraph:
"The secondary lamellae quiver..."
From Keith County Journal by John Janovy Jr.

The secondary lamellae quiver.
Fold upon fold
Might shiver

In the chill of this river
If I wasn't so cold blooded.
Oxygenated water delivers

To my gills, giver
Through the flow
The delirious liquor

My capillaries crave, but bitter
Along with sweet arrives latching bold
In parasitic litter

Coupling with me beastie clever
A courtship dance without consent betrothed,
Consuming, taker never giver.

I whisper
Don't kill the host Don't kill the host
But hope is but a sliver
When the worm doth beg to differ.

Three Sestinas

Raven Leaf Fork Promise Home Word

(A Sestina)

Her name was Raven.
Her hair dark as night and shiny as holly Leaf.
When she spoke, her tongue was a Fork.
In spite of her Promise,
I never knew if she would stay Home.
If it can mean anything, what good is her Word?

Her name was Word.
She told me "evermore" just like the Raven,
Casually dropping the "N" like a Leaf
Just beyond the tine of the Fork,
Unraked unbagged unsecured like her Promise
To stay Home.

Her name was Home.
I dreamed of her in Word
And image, a perching Raven
Eyeing twig and Leaf
To build a nest in the Fork
Of our tree, evermore a Promise.

Her name was Promise.
Would that she stayed Home.
Nevermore true to her Word,
A lifelong mate as Raven
Is wont, but sometimes the Leaf
Falls far from its tree at temptation's Fork.

Her name was Fork,
Impaling Promise,
Fleeing Home,

On broken Word,
Winging into the night, Raven,
Blown whither by the wind, a fallen Leaf.

Her name was Leaf,
A bitter salad eaten with my Fork
Twin tined of fear and Promise.
What is a Home
But just an empty Word
When flown is Raven?

Raven, her page is turned, in Life's book a Leaf.
I wait in the Fork of my tree, A true mate Spring's Promise.
Home is more than where you hang your hat, more than just
a Word.

Book Tree Sympathy Travel Glow Snake

I read a Book
Beneath a Tree
A tragic romance, tea and Sympathy.
My mind to imagined land dothTravel.
My heart races, my skin begins to Glow,
As approaches a Snake.

Are you dread or fascination, oh Snake?
There is no rule for you in this Book.
As you undulate and hang from my Tree,
You entreat me to trust your Sympathy,
As down the trunk you Travel
Your eyes a-Glow.

As night falls and fireflies Glow,
And to the sea a river doth Snake,
And cast upon the garden floor rests Book,
And ripened fruit contemplates a fall fromTree,
And we, entwined in Sympathy,
Far from rationality begin to Travel.

Away! Away! We Travel,
Seeking and finding new haunts until sunrise Glow.
What good are good and evil when Snake
Appends his verse to Book?
When pages are but ink on Tree
What power hath taboo to quench our Sympathy?

Is shared passion really Sympathy
Or merely heated humours Travel
'Til our brains do Glow?
And when we chill, and fever back into its hole doth Snake,
Could we write a novel of remorse, a Book
To fill would take a Tree?

If I plant a Tree,
My heart with earth and sky in Sympathy,
And out his humble plot do Travel,
And dig and plant and dig and plant until with sweat I Glow,
Will want of Snake
Devolve into a dusty chapter in a long forgotten Book?

Inspite of Book, still lurking in each Tree
Him for whom I have no more Sympathy, I seize him ere he
Travel.
Snake steaks Glow on coals for I am hungry, and Snake is
Snake.

Innocent Watch Muddy Blind Post Season:
The Man with the Gun in His Pants
(A Sestina)

He likes to think of himself as innocent.
If he actually kept himself under close watch,
he might find the truth to be a little muddy.
Is he being intentionally blind?
He is, apparently, living in a Post-
Enlightenment season.

He stands his ground on FireWatch.
All the people coming for him look muddy.
Why should he be color blind?
He will not abandon his post!
Should he confess to fear and season
it with self-defense to appear innocent?

For him morality is never muddy.
To anything but black and white he is blind.
You could bind him to a post
in the public square until the change of season,
and he would not profess any liberal or politically innocent
thought while you watch.

"Yea, you are blind!"
he thinks. All the manners of Emily Post
will not justify you in this season
of race war that separates the traitors from the innocent.
He will not stand by and watch
as white culture is diluted and made muddy.

On every wall this message he will post:
Until the season
when we can feel safe from invasion, no one is Innocent.
We must keep watch

until the waters of vengeance wash the muddy
cake from the eyes of those who have been blind.

He has been discontented for many a season.
Reaching into his pants, his hand is innocent
Bystanders in horror watch.
Emotion can be muddy,
but rage when pointed is not blind.
He fires twice, and mortem is post.

They will let him go, innocent or not, just watch!
It is a slippery and muddy slope, but not for those who can
turn a blind
eye to hate and pre-meditation and postpone justice to
another season.

Re: Black Lives Matter Protester Shot Down By White
Supremacist. Omaha 2020

Tears

When they take your hand and look deeply into your eyes and this time there are tears and they say to you "I love you, you know I love you" and maybe that is true or was true once upon a time and they are just now remembering how they loved you but you are leaving and you know that the protestations of love and the tears will be gone tomorrow and if you stay because you think there is still a chance that they may still have a tiny vestige of love in them so maybe you think you should give it another chance but tomorrow will come and they will drift into neglect and they will fall into anger and you will despair tomorrow and tomorrow and if you are honest with yourself you know they do this whenever they sense you are about to leave and really you are already alone so you can't be gone tomorrow you have to take back your hand and be gone now.

First Glance

"There are some people at whom one only has to glance for one's throat to tighten and one's eyes to fill with tears of emotion."
Drive Your Plow Over The Bones Of The Dead by Olga Tokarczuk

It was not the first glance.
The first glance of her,
Sitting there,
Dressed in black cashmere,
Sipping the glass of happy hour special cabernet sauvignon,
Talking about renting a villa in Provence,
And inviting her friends and family
To share the sun of southern France,
Resulting in a raised eyebrow of interest.

The throat tightening
And eyes filled with tears
Came somewhat later.
A moment when
I wasn't glancing at her.
No,
Not just glancing,
But looking deeply into her eyes,
Not just beside her,
But reaching out and touching her hand
And having her wrap her fingers around mine.

It is years and years later,
And maybe my eyes don't fill with tears,
But I still get that tightness in the throat
And the catch in the breath
And the gooseflesh
Whenever her hand welcomes mine.

Dead Man Walking

Well, it looks like this will be my last day of walking on this
earth.
I've fallen, and I can't get up.

I have walked every day.
Every day of my life since I first got up on two feet when I
was a baby.

People who see me walking probably think,
"What is wrong with that guy?"
Not an unreasonable reaction.
None of the joints work right anymore,
all stiff and cranky,
rough,
screaming at me when I move around.
When I walk,
my arms are out like wings,
giving me what little balance I have left to work with.
I swing one leg out and around and back down, planting it
before I tip over.
Then the other leg.
I look like a drunk on stilts.
The whole mechanism which worked so beautifully when I
was a kid,
hips knees ankles feet,
is wrecked.
Even my hands are getting curled and gnarled.

Too much crawling around in tight spaces and falling from
high places.
Hitting things.
Bruises, tears, sprains, fractures,
crookedly healed shot through with arthritis.
I suppose that, if you had told me I would be crippled by the
age of fifty,

I would have avoided a career in the building trades,
been something less physically destructive, like a college
professor.
But then, all that time inside, all that time with books,
all that time with people not as smart as they think they are,
I wouldn't have been able to stand for that.
Better to make a run of it,
hard work by hard men for hard money.
Work hard play hard. That's the life.

I am lying here on the ground.
That last stride, my last step,
I didn't stick the landing,
my ankle rolled, my head hit the pavement.
I think of Nadia, so pretty, she always stuck the landing.
Whatever happened to Nadia?
Blood seeps from my ear.

The old woman is coming with the wheelchair.
She is cursing.
She is cursing me for being a cripple,
and here she is in her golden years,
when she is supposed to playing bingo at the senior center
and courting rich widowers,
but no, she has to babysit her crippled child who,
if he had paid attention in school, could have been a college
professor like his father,
you stupid son of a bitch.

I see the blood from my ear trickle past my eye and think,
"You're right, momma, you're right."

Chronodislogical

(pseudo-autobiographical episodes recounted out of order)

In 1950, I told my mother
That I was not ready to leave the womb.
She ignored my plea
And cast me out of my dark warm Eden
Into the bright cold outland
Where there is weeping and wailing and gnashing of teeth.
I didn't even have any teeth to gnash,
But I could weep and wail with the best.

In 2016, a bird impaled on a cactus
Looked at me with eye of terror and entreaty,
How much longer would you have lived,
Dear Bird,
Attached to prickly mate,
Had I not gently tugged the barb
From your breast
And blood flowed out
Unstanchable
As I laid you to rest
Among the lilies?

In 1957, I was scarred for life
In a tragi-comic playground Civil War re-enactment.
Nobody called an ambulance.
I hobbled about all day,
Then limped down the side of the mountain,
Cartilage in my knee shredded.
I did not know 'til then
That friends, in war, choose other sides
And lose all sense of who we were.

In 1963, in Mr. Wisniewski's music class,
His story of auditioning for the Lawrence Welk Show

Was interrupted by the announcement
That our President had been shot.
Johnny Velasquez, who was sitting at the desk next to mine,
Threw himself to the floor and cried out,
"Nothing will ever be the same."
His tears fell on my right shoe.

In 1988, my Father's funeral besmirched
By their gross impropriety,
My blood boiled.
They allowed Her to attend,
Nay, invited Her,
Nay, housed and feted her,
While I slept in my car.
My Father came to me in a dream.
"Forgive them," He said, "for they know not what they do."
"They know exactly what they do," I said.
I buried His ghost.
I no longer appeared in family pictures.

In 1953, I waited on the front porch,
Waited for the Easter Bunny.
I wasn't satisfied with the colored eggs and chocolate candy.
I wanted the Bunny.
Finally, my parents told me there was no Easter Bunny.
It was a lie,
An innocent lie to entertain and distract a child
For a few days each spring.
I was disappointed momentarily, then relieved.
Waiting was unsatisfying.
They told me many more lies over the years,
More serious lies,
Lies they never admitted were lies,
Lies that were ultimately unsatisfying.

In 1993, She told me,
"Do not write me poetry.

Do not sing me songs of love.
Do not bring me donuts on our anniversary."
I replied, "This is what I do.
This is who I am."
She said, "It's too much.
It makes a demand on Me which I am unable to fulfill.
Stop."
I found other ways to make her unhappy with my love.

In 2000, just before she died,
My Mother gave me
An album of photographs
Each labeled with names and dates,
All the family reunions, birthdays, weddings, vacations
I had missed over the years,
All the events I hadn't attended
and to which I had not been invited.
Forgiveness was never begged.
This book a criticism of me
For naming Their sin.
The cold bright light on the pale body in the morgue
Did not inspire weeping,
Only wonder why I hadn't wanted to leave in the beginning.

Considerate Admirer

She could tell he was looking, even though he tried to be unobvious about it.

. . . .

She had punched off the alarm on her phone and drifted off, then she awoke with a start. Shit! Shit! Shit! If the hour hadn't been late, she wouldn't have been in a rush. But she didn't like being late for work, hated being late, really.

So she grabbed the first pair of jeans she came across in the closet. There was a pair on top of the sock basket. It was Friday, casual dress day, at the office. As she pulled on the jeans, she smiled. These were the comfortable ones.

. . . .

She felt his eyes on her again as she walked past his cubicle.

She forgot, until she was making her rounds through the office distributing the mail, that the comfortable jeans had a hole in them. It was just down and to the left of the right rear pocket, just big enough to be noticeable, just big enough for someone who was looking to see the fuchsia nylon of her underwear.

Yes, she could feel his eyes on her. She heard some people giggling and whispering among themselves as she passed by. Fine. Whatever. But this guy, Bill in Materials Management, the intensity of his gaze was palpable. Up to now, he had never made a suggestive comment or tried anything gross. She couldn't even remember him making eye contact with her as she handed him his mail. Was she imagining him watching her? Was this a hostile work environment? No. This guy was the opposite of hostile. But...

. . . .

What is the fascination with a holey pair of old jeans, he wondered? Of course, it wasn't just that was it? It was the denim shaped into a certain curve. It was the glimpse of something underneath. And it was that something underneath formed around flesh. The flesh. How could one concentrate on production forecasting data?

He had never been attracted to any of the women in the office before. He wondered just this past Sunday if that article in the Times about asexuality applied to him. And this woman from the mailroom, he had seen her every day for years. Now. NOW! A particular hole in a particular place in a particular pair of old jeans revealing a particular shade of hot pink was making him interested...crazy.

What was her name? Sandy? Sandra? No, Cassandra, that was it.

. . . .

She found his note among the outgoing mail...an envelope with her name on it... very precise printing with a fine tipped pen.

Cassandra.
Please do not take offense. I have no intention of disrespecting you or making you uncomfortable.
I will be at the Wooden Nickel after work having a glass of wine. This is my usual habit, as it is a quiet, relaxing, and friendly place. Please join me.
If you choose not to, I will make no further entreaties, and life will go on as before.
Sincerely,
A Considerate Admirer

. . . .

He sat in his usual booth at The Wooden Nickel. He had a view of the front door. When she walked in, he stood. She walked over and sat down.

"You came," he said.

"Well," she said, "I've never experienced a pickup line that started with an apology-slash-disclaimer. I was curious."

"Would you like a drink? They have a serviceable Chardonnay here, if you like wine."

"You don't oversell anything, do you?" She saw him blush.

"I'm not much of a drinker, but a light beer would be OK."

He went to the bar and got her a beer.

She took a sip and said, "I felt your eyes on me today. I wasn't sure if I should feel creeped out or flattered or what."

"Or what, yeah," he said. "When you walked past my cubicle, it was like some switch in my brain got flipped, and sitting across from you, talking over drinks, became immensely important. I don't know how to explain it."

"Well, I don't know where you think this is going, but I'm not in the market for a relationship, especially with somebody at work," she replied.

"That's fine," he said. "Just being here now with you is enough. Thanks."

She finished her beer, got up and left. "Wow!" she said to herself as she exited the bar.

Bill ordered another Chardonnay.

. . . .

The next Friday, Bill was working on cost averaging data to facilitate wholesale pricing review.

Cassandra stopped at his desk and handed him his mail. He didn't look up.

As she walked away, he glanced at her back. She was wearing an old sweatshirt. The neck was stretched out just enough to reveal one bra strap, a particular shade of turquoise pressing into the flesh of her shoulder. The flesh. "Wow!" he said to himself.

He logged off on his computer, took a sheet of paper and his fine tipped pen, and started writing...Cassandra...
She would be back for outgoing mail in what now seemed an eternity.

Rush Hour

I don't know why they call it rush hour.
Even under the best of conditions
We crawl along
Congested
If we were rushing
It would be rush 20 minutes
Today no one is rushing anywhere
We are all sitting in our cars
Perfectly still
Not moving forward backward or sideways

All the coffee
Wakeup cup
Breakfast cup
Travel mug usually lasts until downtown
But is almost gone
And we're still miles from the office
Where the bathroom is
At this rate of caffeinated liquid consumption
My bladder has about one hour
before it reaches capacity
So rushing would be good

I tap my foot
I cross my legs
I think I can do this
Just relax

The guy in the car in front of me
Rolls down his window
And dumps coffee out of his travel mug
Then he looks around
And seems to be struggling
like a contortionist in a small box

In my rearview mirror
The guy behind me is doing the same thing

I get it
Not wanting to be so obvious
I chug the dregs of my coffee
Unzip
It's tricky and I'm nervous
It's a semi-public place
Wait for it
Wait for it

OMG
The traffic unsnarls ahead
Honking behind
Give a guy a break
What's the rush?

Rushing Things

She struck him with the flat of her hand, palm side, fingers fully extended, every muscle and sinew tight in expectation of impact with his face. She could have clawed him with her fingernails or punched him in the nose. Would the scratch have just inflamed him? Would the punch have provoked retaliation? Was the open-handed slap more demeaning (degrading? emasculating?)? Focus, Deborah! There's a man in front of you that you just hit!

She addressed the shock and awe that she sensed filling the space between them. "You're rushing things, Tom, knowingly rushing things, assuming things." she paused. He touched the reddening mark on his cheek and furrowed his eyebrows. "Considering the lateness of the hour," she continued, "you should probably go."

It was their second date. He hadn't really done anything untoward. He was presenting as Mr. Nice Guy, but she could see down the road, see where it was going. Her heart was pounding. He leaned in, just a little, a barely perceptible lean, but it was there, testing the waters. Her brain lurched.

She could see that he would tell her that she was pretty, even though her nose was obviously just wrong, and her chin was weak, and her legs were too short for the length of her torso, and her hair was the kind of hair that you just couldn't do anything with, and she was awfully thin. Eventually, she would invite him into her apartment, and he would tell her that she was clever, even though she never finished high school, and didn't appreciate the arts (were romance novels art?), and she worked at a C-store out on the highway (was hoping to advance to assistant manager too lofty a goal?). She would want to hear all those compliments from him, even though she knew they were just lies.

Then there would be the first tentative kiss and the furtive touching and the fumbling with buttons and zippers and the closing of eyes and the wondering how this happens, and you aren't even sure if you want it to, but you don't stop it. And then he is using your bathroom and flushing the toilet and coming back into your bed (and did you see his fingernails? They're never really clean!)

This was not a long series of ruminative thoughts for Deborah. It was a sudden bursting of ideational fireworks, an epiphany. The planting of her back foot, the rotation of her hips, the transfer of weight, the follow through in the extension of her arm toward his face (just like Master Ho at the New Feminist Dojo had taught her) were an unconscious and irresistible impulse.

Tom took a knee and tried to control his breathing (just like his high school football coach had taught him). His heart was beating way too fast. He couldn't see down the road, not even a little, not at all.

All evening he had been swimming in a sea of ruminative thought. Over drinks she had said he was cute, even though he was balding and overweight, and, in a hurry to get to the bar on time, he had forgotten to trim the nest of hairs growing out of his ears. She had said she wanted to meet someone nice for a change, and, even though he was anxious and clearly emotionally needy, he had tried to project a strong but considerate manliness. Was she pretending to be impressed by his community college associates degree and his job as a Jiffy Lube shop manager? Did she really care that he embraced diversity, hiring a black guy and a lesbian and an ex-con and a Guatemalan refugee with suspicious documentation to work for him? He thought wistfully about kissing and furtive touching and buttons and zippers. He thought he should have gotten some women's clothing to practice on so he wouldn't fumble his chance, if it came, but how would you explain women's clothing in your closet, if she ever came over to your place. He thought about his fingernails as they Uber-ed to her place (They were never clean. Nothing at Jiffy Lube was clean.). He thought maybe he shouldn't have had that second double espresso after dinner.

He was leaning in to ask her if he could use her bathroom when her hand burst into his brain like fireworks.

He took a knee. He touched the hot, reddening blotch on his cheek.

Oh, Jesus! She couldn't tell if he was praying or about to propose.

Tom looked up at her. One tiny tear leaked from his left eye. "So, Deborah, you're thinking we should take it slow?"

"Oh, my God, Tom! I'm so sorry! I don't know what came over me." Her heart slowed, and the adrenaline ebbed. "Please come in, and we'll see what we can do about those fingernails. I mean your face."

"Thanks. I could really use a bathroom right now."

Airport

He is a retired orthopedic surgeon with a year's worth of Viagra in his suitcase and time on his hands.

She is a professionally trained dancer with an appreciation of the physical side of life and time to kill before her next engagement.

He is flying from Florida to Canada.
She is flying from Ireland to California.

They are walking toward each other in the concourse of the International Terminal.
They glance in each other's direction.
He slows down and thinks, "Hmmmm."
She slows down and thinks, "Hmmmm."

He checks his watch. How much time before his flight?
She checks her phone. Her gate has changed.

They are past each other.
They both smile and pick up the pace.
It was a nice thought.

Gullible

Am I a tragic figure? I admit that I am gullible. Repeatedly gullible. Unremittingly gullible.

Maybe you think my gullibility flows from a gushing font of stupidity, that anybody would or should know better, and, therefore, I get no sympathy points from you for my outcomes.

Maybe you are right. Yet you stood by through thick and thin. You have been nice. People can be nice.
I really, really want to believe in the goodness of other people. I want to believe that being nice to someone elicits niceness in return. Is that so wrong?
Ok, so you knew who I was dating, and you said, "Oooh! Wow! Be careful!"
When we got engaged, you said, "Oh, no! Don't do it! For the love of god, stop!"
When we got married, you refused to come to the wedding. No gift. Just an envelope with a lawyer's business card inside.

Ok. Thanks. With that lawyer's help it only took five years to recover from the bankruptcy. And thanks for letting me live in your basement. Most of my so-called friends just looked away from this train wreck of a life that I laid at your feet.

So here we go again! I'm dating.
Yes, I'll be careful.
No, I can't come over right now.
Yes, he borrowed my car to go visit the kid he had with his ex-girlfriend.
No, he'll only use my debit card to get gas.
Yes, he's picking the kid up at the casino where she works.
What? Please don't say, "For the love of god!"

Distracted

She noticed that, when he kissed her, he didn't seem as engaged. It was different, she was sure of it. She wasn't just feeling down on herself. It was him. He was distracted. Even when she tried to hold the kiss a little longer, press in a little harder, he would pat her on the butt and pull away. She had seen him pat the family dog on the butt like that when he didn't want to play tug of war with the old sock, only wanted to read his newspaper and drink his tumbler of Scotch.

This made her question her entire existence with this man. Had she been wrong about him from the start? Had all that passionate kissing in the old days been his attempt to appear passionate? Had she been clumsy and over-wrought and absent of any sense of reading the emotional weather?

She was a believer in kissing. To her, kissing was the litmus test of a relationship's quality. There had been really good kissing. How could she have got it wrong?

And what was the point of pretending anyway? Either you had it, or you didn't. If you didn't have it, what was the point of hanging around with someone you didn't like all that much?

And she really had liked him. Really liked him! He was physically gorgeous and smart and said nice things and had his own money. They did so many amazing things together in the early days. He would kiss her as if he meant it.

She was thinking about packing her suitcases as she looked at the man, the Scotch, the newspaper, the dog. Just as she was turning to go to the bedroom to do exactly that, he said, "Darling, I'm sorry I've been so distracted lately. I haven't said anything to you about this, but my parents are getting divorced after thirty years of what I thought was blissful marriage."

"Oh, darling!" she gasped.

"I know," he said. "It's so shocking. I just haven't been able to process it. How could I have been so dense, so clueless about the emotional weather? It's made me question my whole emotional universe."

She went to him, took away the Scotch and the newspaper, threw the dog's old sock down the hall, and pulled him up off the couch. She kissed him deeply, passionately.

"That's truly devastating, my love, but we will get through this together," she said. "You and me. You'll never have to worry about us." He kissed her back, just like in the old days. "That's great, darling!", he said. "They're going to have to sell the house and split the proceeds. My mother will need a place to stay until she can get back on her feet."

She patted him on the butt and pulled away, thinking about those suitcases.

Africa

I was sitting with my friend, Todd, at the local bar having a drink. I reminisced about my father's Africa fixation. He wanted to go to Africa and help create sites where safe drinking water could be obtained. He would get this far away look in his eyes and wax eloquent about his sense of mission.

We never went to Africa.

It would have involved moving not only himself but also his wife and three children. His wife, my mother, said, "Hell no!" She also said, "Are you crazy?" She also said some things behind closed doors that I didn't clearly understand, although I did try to eavesdrop. It involved shouting and throwing things.

"What if that had actually happened?" Todd asked. "Can you imagine being dropped into West Africa in the '60's?"

"I can't imagine it."

"Sure you can," he said. "Change a thing or two just a little bit. Maybe your father is a little more persuasive. Maybe your mother is a little less fearful. Maybe he gets offered an actual job with a well-funded international charity. Maybe your parents talk to some people who have worked overseas and found it challenging but rewarding."

"Nope. It was a dream he could have to hold the moral high ground. It was a dream my mother could deny him to hold the power in the marriage."

"C'mon, man, unleash the inner adventurous youth you keep locked up inside that over-intellectualized head!" said Todd.

I lifted my glass and caught the bartender's eye. "I'll need some more tequila!"

I am digging wells and carrying water. I discover that I have a gift for languages. It doesn't take me long to pick up enough of the local dialect to be able to communicate with the lovely, clever, and hysterically funny Africans. Even though I am just a teenageer, I am conscripted by the headman of the village to teach English to the kids in the little one-room school.

This is obviously a dream, a dream dreamed by a totally naive American white kid, filled with every stereotype and misconception a wooden head can have.

Then I see her. She is not much older than I am, a little older, enough older to make her mysterious, possibly deadly to one's better judgment, and irresistibly attractive. She is tall, slim, with prominent cheekbones, and elegant in movement. She talks to the locals about the history and the political philosophy of liberation.

My father is digging wells and installing filtration equipment. My mother is staffing a medical clinic.

She is the daughter of the Soviet agricultural attache. Our paths cross at a variety of venues...the school, the village garden, the wasteland commandeered for a soccer pitch, a reception at the embassy.

My desire for justice, my sympathy for the working class, my dedication to the elimination of exploitation and poverty, my background in Christian democratic socialism exceed her expectations. Her interest in American books, movies, and music exceed my expectations.

We flirt, work, teach, play, flirt.

We contemplate how to seduce each other, but it's complicated, because neither of us is really free. We are both seeking asylum in the other's world.

My mother and her mother want to go home. Both embassies are nervous. Her father and my father meet to figure out how to cool off what they perceive to be an awkward romance. We ask each other, "Where would we run, if we could run away?"

An old woman at the well pats my shoulder as I draw off a bucket of crystal clear water from the tap on the purification equipment. My beautiful Russian fellow traveler reenacts George Washington crossing the Delaware with the village children.

As I stare in wonder at this goddess walking among us, the old woman whispers in my ear, "Water, earth, sun, plants. Everything else is vanity."

I roll over and refocus on cheekbones.

The Lingering Presence of Fear

Menlo Adair stepped into the coat closet and closed the door.
It was just barely big enough for him among the boots and
shoes and jackets. He sat on the floor and closed his eyes. As
he tried to control his heartbeat and breathing, he smelled the
familiar smells of leather and mink oil and dirt and sweat
infused cotton. It was the first time he had entered the closet
voluntarily. Ever.

Menlo had always been locked in his small bedroom or in a
closet or in a plywood box in the basement. Ever since his
mother had disappeared, he and his father had lived, just the
two of them, in this old farm house in the middle of Kansas.
Menlo had never been put in a coffin and buried alive, but he
imagined it, knew in his heart of hearts that it was coming.

The vision of his father's face appeared before him like the
Great and Terrible OZ. He knew what came next. His eyes
snapped open and he shuddered.

Menlo was not a bad kid. He had never been oppositional or
destructive or disrespectful. Phil Adair was no connoisseur of
goodness. Menlo shook his head. Maybe his father hated
goodness, wanted to crush the goodness in him. He tried to
conjure up his mother's face, a good face, a smiling face, a
loving face.

What Menlo really liked was being outdoors. He liked grass
and trees and flowers and water and birds. His mother would

take him to the park down by the river. He would play until he was exhausted, then he would lie down with his head in his mother's lap, and she would read stories to him, sometimes in French. Menlo relaxed a little, feeling the memory of the expansiveness of green space and sky and the lilt in his mother's voice. "Je suis perdu," he thought to himself..

His father had told the young boy that his mother had run off with the high school French teacher, abandoned them. Since then he was always inside, not even able to look out. Plywood boarded up windows, locked doors. Didn't anybody wonder why he wasn't in school? Menlo contemplated the horrors that happened to people every day in the middle of America, land of the free and home of the brave, and nobody did anything about it. Well, maybe after it was too late somebody investigated. You either took care of your own shit and survived, or you didn't.

Maybe he had watched too many cop shows on TV and read too many serial killer books. Of course he had. That was all there was in the old house on the farmstead. Him, a sensitive and impressionable child, and his father, a hard, lonely man. Menlo supposed you were supposed to identify with the persevering cops or the clever detectives, but he could see his father's eyes light up when the killer was performing his evil deeds. Menlo identified with the victims, scarred for life by what happened to them or their innocent lives cut short. Menlo saw his father look at him, an innocent life at the mercy of a dark force. He could sense that his time would come.

Menlo was no longer a little kid. He ate what food his father provided. From prison movies he knew the pushups and squats and calisthenics you did to get stronger. He calculated how long it would take him to get big enough to take down his father. He was sure his father was making those same calculations.

Had his mother really run off with the high school French teacher as his father had said? Was she, or were they somewhere? In Paris, or maybe tied up, tortured, buried in a plywood box out on the south forty? He had been so young when she vanished.

In the closet in the dark, Menlo closed his eyes. He let the vision come to him. He let himself fall into the fear. His father's eyes alight, the crooked leering smile, the hands around his throat. It was the time. He reached for the bronze statuette of the ballet dancer on the end table and struck his father again and again. In the closet, in the dark, he felt the solidity of the sculpture in his hand. His mother had bought it at a flea market for him before she was gone. It gave him a sense of comfort. Maybe tomorrow he would go outside. He floated away into sleep.

Sun

I call him in Santa Barbara.

His official title is "caretaker." He's a pimply faced white kid high school dropout short order cook that I rescued from a lifetime of grease at Joe's Diner. He is funny and smart and the most reliable person I know.

"Hello, famous lady," he says. I can hear him smile. He is the master of the self-deprecating conceit-puncturing inside joke. The house overlooks the Pacific where I almost never am. But I can't give it up. There is an orange tree in the yard, and I can sit on the deck and drink a cup of espresso and eat an orange off my own tree and watch the sun sink into the ocean, where I wish I was right now. I have the life that many people dream of, but it is a life that was designed for me by other people.

"Messages?" I ask.

"Mr. Doyle called, Miss. He will be at the Hotel Angleterre until the Mistral makes itself unbearable."

"Thank you, Jonah."

"Are you coming home, Miss, or responding to his summons."

"I don't view it as a summons, Jonah, but I have a few open days after Paris."

"Be careful, Miss."

"Always, Jonah."

There is no time frame. Just the wind. It is getting into Autumn.

He knows where I am, and how long it would take to get to him. He knows that I will respond to the announcement of his location. Not even an invitation, really. A summons.

Of course, he knows. Fashion Week has just ended.

There is a train from Paris to Marseilles every half hour. It takes a little over three hours. Then a car back up the Rhone.

I check the weather forecast in Provence. Wind from the Northeast. 30kph with gusts higher. Overcast. Light rain. What is unbearable for him? He thinks I know what is unbearable for him. He thinks I will bear what is unbearable for me.

There is the possibility of a photo shoot for a perfume ad, stills and video, if I stay in Paris for another week. It involves filmy dresses and floating in water. Venues are being negotiated. It is warm and sunny here. I should not go to meet him. I should stay and work.

I call Natalya at the agency. She tells me the perfume shoot is off. Mr. Doyle has offered Rachel, and they have accepted. So I am free to travel. Yes, Mr. Doyle has made arrangements. The train. The cars. Security detail. He will book a room in the Europa, a half hour's walk from the Angleterre. Of course. How discreet.
"Thank you, Rachel. Tell Mr. Doyle I will meet with him."
"As you wish, Miss."
As I wish! If only...

I am always happy to avoid him for considerable lengths of time. There are things between us that will never be resolved, never be forgiven. Forgiveness is only useful if you wish to salvage a relationship. A reunion is likely to have traumatic results. Doyle is wrong about bearing the unbearable. There is always more than the unbearable to bear. One must also bear the scars that remain after the unbearable damage is done.

But, then again, I am packing my suitcases and heading South.

I sleep in. I have a late breakfast in the hotel courtyard garden. Yogurt, fresh fruit, half a croissant, black coffee. I think about how to manage our interactions so that I don't have to be in the same room alone with him. Not for my safety. For his. I have grudges, resentments, revenge fantasies that need expression.

The car service arrives. A driver and two security personnel. A man and woman. I have worked with them before. They are good. Efficient, competent, unobtrusive. The agency has provided security ever since the incident in Berlin. It is a busy day in Paris. The driver uses several socially unacceptable techniques to get us to the train on time. Security does not want loitering in large open spaces, so we have to press the limits. The car drops us off exactly twelve minutes before the TGV departs. We walk briskly through the terminal, find the rail car, park the luggage, and take our seats.

I love the train in France. Whatever anxiety I feel, it melts away as we float along through the countryside. Can a person feel at home in a foreign country, want to find a way to stay, shrug off the life that brought one to this point? Choose something for oneself?

People look. They try not to stare. They see that I am not traveling alone. They go back to their electronic devices. Maybe Googling "Sun." Three teenage girls who can't resist the urge to say hello get autographs with sharpie on their backpacks.

I don't read or text or game or sleep. I watch the land. It's different now than it was in the spring, when everything was new and fresh and everything seemed possible. Now the browns and greys are taking over. Things are shutting down, protecting themselves against the coming winter.

At Gare de Marseilles-St. Charles, a woman in black holds a sign with my name on it. "SUN." We move briskly through the station. We drive north.

"Bonsoir, mademoiselle. Welcome to Hotel Europa. Your suite is ready for you. My name is Jacque. I am at your disposal for anything you may need."
Security personnel will be in the next room.
"Merci. Please contact the Angleterre, Jacque, and confirm that M. Paul Doyle is in residence. If so, leave instructions for him to be at a table in the hotel restaurant at 2000h tomorrow."
"As you wish, mademoiselle."

I call Santa Barbara.
"Hello, pretty boss lady."
"I am at The Europa."
"You could come home and prune the hedges. I could go to Provence and deal with Mr. Doyle. I've been taking judo lessons." I can see him striking a pose.
"Easy now, Cato."
"Be careful out there, boss."
"Always."

The Angleterre. Doyle has already ordered wine and appetizers. He swirls and holds the glass up to catch the light in a certain way.

"The day I found you in The Koreatown market," Doyle says, "you were this beautiful girl. The most beautiful girl. 'Pick me the most perfect plum.' was what I said to you. Why did I say that? But you knew. You had the insight into what was just pretty and what was the full experience of what a plum should be. To this day, it is the single most delicious thing I have ever eaten. I went back to my hotel room and wept."
I remember.

Korean mother. American father. They met when he was stationed with the peacekeepers near the DMZ. My mother was a rural girl. He was lonely. She wanted a way out of poverty. His tour of duty ended. He went back to America. She was pregnant. The family was shamed. She was exiled to the ex-pat enclave in LA. She was out, but not out of poverty.

Paul Doyle found us. He made a contract with my mother for exclusive representation. I was tall for my age. 12. I only modeled children's clothes briefly. There was a teen fashion mag cover when I was 14. That made New York possible. Paul said into the phone to his friend who wrote a column in the Times, "She is exotic and familiar all at the same time."

Fourteen years old in New York City. Doyle was my agent, my manager, my landlord, my protector. Before we left LA, he told my mother, "No one touches her." Really? The work was always there, the demand for this girl, this young woman, this girl, this teenager, this woman, this girl. I was all of them. He picked the jobs, the photogs, the dressers, the makeup artists, the hairdressers. He was guiding, supporting, comforting, grounding, reproving, parental. But when I caught him unawares, there was a look when he looked at me, like the look when he bit into the perfect plum.

We are sitting in the dining room of The Angleterre. The wind has abated. The doors are open. There are stars in the sky above the tops of the trees. A piano plays lightly in the background. There are white linen tablecloths and candles. It would be romantic under other circumstances.

We never had a sexual relationship. He never discussed his sex life with me. I asked around. Everyone in the fashion world who knew him described him as having a series of sexual partners, but these were relatively brief liaisons.

This didn't stop Doyle from actively interfering in my personal life. He perceived relationships as dangers to the advancement of my career in modeling. Attachments got in the way of being open to assignments. Attachments undermined his power over me. Attachments meant the possibility of pregnancy or sexually transmitted diseases. If he knew of my attraction to anyone, he would ruthlessly attack that person until they withdrew. What he did to Bobby...

My mother died the year I was twenty-one. Every manager of modeling talent in the world pursued me. Did I want to leave Doyle? I did, but Doyle offered me a contract for exclusive representation. He wouldn't take any money from me. He would receive a commission directly from the producer or designer or photographer or magazine for arranging my presence where it was required. My fee for modeling was a separate negotiation which he also handled. There was lots of money.

He reaches across the table and touches my hand. I flinch but don't withdraw.
"My Sun," he says, then withdraws his hand to muffle a cough.
"The woman at the table across the room is watching you intently," I say. "How voyeuristic for her."
He stops coughing, has a drink of water, and says, "She's my nurse."
"No need for euphemisms between us, Paul."
"I'm dying."
I laugh.
"Literally," he says.

I call Santa Barbara.
Jonah answers. "It's Bobby's birthday, Boss."
"As if I didn't remember."
"Do you want me to send the usual to Forest Lawn?"
"Something bigger this year. Something with plums."
"Is Mr. Doyle dead yet, Miss?"
"Not yet, but soon, I think."
"No court in the world will convict you."

"Good night, Jonah."

For a time Rachel, another model, shared an apartment with me in Brooklyn. For some reason, Doyle left her alone. I thought.

"Have you ever been to Doyle's place?" she asked one night.

"No," I said with an unnecessary iciness.

"I have," she said. "Wow!"

"How 'wow?'"

"I think he had the idea that I would want to see his etchings. That we would be a thing. I was sure he knew I wasn't into guys, but maybe we would be some kind of odd couple anyway."

"So did you see his etchings?"

"He didn't have etchings. He had pictures of you. Everywhere. Big ones on the walls. Little ones on ledges and tables. All your old campaigns and covers. Headshots of you as a girl. It was like a Sun Shrine. I thought to myself, 'Why doesn't she just get it over with and fuck this guy? Then we could all get on with our lives.'"

"That is never going to happen!"

"Sure. Of course not," Rachel continued. "He was mixing drinks, talking about how much he respected my work, blah, blah, blah. I exited, stage left. Left him standing there talking to the martini shaker."

"Your rejection of him might cost you jobs," I worried.

"Are you kidding! I have more jobs than ever."

We are in a car, some brutish British four wheel drive thing. Doyle and I are in the back. The nurse is in the front passenger seat. Security guy is driving. Security gal is in the chase car. We are winding our way out of the river valley into the hillier countryside.

"Global warming is raising the average temperatures, which is not good for the grapes. The higher the elevation of the

vineyard, assuming that the soil composition is right, makes
survivability more likely," Doyle opined.
I looked out the window. Grapevines, grapevines, tangled
grapevines wrestled into tidy rows..

We are off the pavement on a rocky dirt track.
"I have been coming to Provence for more than ten years,
buying wine, getting to know the people, studying the land,
learning the mysterious ways of the vignerons."
We drive up this narrow path to a villa at the top of a hill. We
get out.
"Normally a place like this would never be for sale. It has
been in the same family for three hundred years. The old man
is feeling his age. His son is a civil engineer working on
transportation infrastructure in Spain. His daughter is a
banker in Milan. Neither has any children."
"It's very lovely, Paul. What does it have to do with me?"
"You are the new owner, my dear Sun."

We sit on the patio of the villa. The old man brings out wine
and cheese and bread. I ask for water. The leaves on the
grapevines are turning gold and orange and red.
"My cancer has metastasized," Paul says. "When I leave here,
I am going to Switzerland. I will stay there in hospice. I will
be dead in a month or so, probably."
Why am I crying? Good riddance is what I tell myself Ifeel.
"There are ten hectares of grapes here. There is another
packet of land, considered by many to be less desirable, but
could be developed if you find the right varietals. There are
contracts with other vineyards to supply grapes for blending
to achieve the end product that you want. In addition to the
house, there is a production facility on the grounds and a cave
for barrel aging. Francois will stay on to advise you for a time,
but he will be going to Spain to live with his son at some
point in the near future. You will have to find a winemaker to

hire to run the operations. I will leave you a file of the interviews I have conducted."

I have nothing to say to all this. What is there to say? He presents it as a fait accompli.

We drive back. The wind is up. It pushes the beast of a car around. The driver looks grim as he tries to keep us on the narrow French country roads. Doyle looks out the window as if it is the last time with an old friend. He coughs into a handkerchief. I look out my window as if it is the first time. The land remains where it is as we roll past. It can't be anywhere else other than where it is.

"Why would I want this, Paul?"

"You are still beautiful, still in demand, but you are twenty nine. Your mother is dead. You haven't been home in months. You have to use your intelligence, your insight, to see what is next. A photo of you at forty will not pay the rent. It is time to put down roots. That is the way of the world."

"It's too much. You are always choosing for me." Tears leak unbidden from my eyes. "It is unbearable."

"It is not nearly enough. I was no big deal before I met you. Everything I have, everything, is because of you, your work, the other work that your work brought to me. I don't need it now. It all goes back to the source. You love the French countryside. You think I don't know you? Nothing else would be right."

"Why a vineyard?"

"Food will always be the most important need. Wine will always be the most important food. People will want wine when they are together and when they are alone. They will want it when they are happy and when they are sad. They will want it if they are rich or they are poor. They will want it before, during, and after a meal, and when there is nothing at all to eat. The terroir of France is the heart of wine. It is handing you back the perfect plum so that you can eat it."

"When are you coming back?" asks Jonah.

"How soon can you be in Marseilles?"

"Marseilles? Are you needing my judo skills?"

"No. Mr. Doyle is gone. I need your house management skills."

"There is a house?"

"Yes. And lots of pruning to be done."

Romeo and Juliet: After the Crypt

Romeo: Ah, Shakespeare,
you are such a dear, dear silly goose,
your ending to our story suspending all claims on credulity,
but dramatic it was,
and time was running on, and you needed to get the curtain down,
and so you offed us.
Ah, Will! We were alive, if not so well,
so this tale I tell.

Forsooth and verily,
Romeo and Juliet did not die there, fools in love.
The stars were set against us, yet we survived..

In lovely old Verona.
We met. We fell in love.
The Friar, a curious ally, had a rather liberal view of sexuality and marriage.
We were secretly married, although she had been promised by her parents to creepy old Paris. We spent the night together.
It was violins and nightingales. It was passionate young love. True. True.
Then I must flee to Mantua, exiled by the Prince for feuding and deadly swordplay.
I tell her "I'll be back as soon as I am able." Yes. Yes.

A plague is ravaging Northern Italy. The Black Death has been rolling through the country in waves for over a hundred years. The doctors think they have beaten it back, but then it flares up again. Our only weapon is to separate the sick from the well. Just as I get to Mantua, they close the gates of the city and declare another quarantine. Nobody in or out until this spike in cases burns itself out. Juliet is back in Verona, defenseless against the social machinations of her parents. Months go by.

Romeo knocks at the door of the Capulet home.

Nurse: Ah! Young Montague!

Romeo: I must see Juliet!

Nurse: Are you not banished from these environs?

Romeo: The Prince's ban is not enough to hold me forever.

Capulet (from inside the house): Nurse, who calls on us at this hour?

Nurse: Only a woeful beggar!

Capulet: Send him away and bar the door.

Nurse (to Romeo in whisper): It is not safe. Go to the garden. I will tell my lady you await her there.

Juliet (from her balcony): So the young outlaw finally finds the courage to return to the scene of the crime!

Romeo: It is no crime to love you, wife.

Juliet (laughs): Is it not the greatest of crimes to love and leave and not return and leave me to the predations of evil forces? I am not your wife! While you are vacationing in foreign climes, I am wed to Paris. Look at me! I am ruined! (She places her hands on her rounded belly.)

Romeo: You are with child!

Juliet: The world turns, even in your absence.

Romeo: Am I not your rightful husband and this child's father?

Juliet: Do you think your seed is planted without opposition? Your arrogance is only exceeded by your ignorance! It was but three days from your abandonment that Paris was gifted my person by my parents, the Prince, the Church. My cries for mercy have no effect, especially in the marriage chamber. I am his property now, and this child is his legal progeny.

Romeo (unsheathing his sword): I shall take you back.

Juliet: Put that thing away! Is your willful feuding and careless swordplay not what ripped us apart? This tragedy has made you no wiser. Begone! I have no use for silly boys.

(Juliet withdraws. Romeo, downcast, departs)

Two years pass. Romeo lives in exile in Mantua. His wealthy parents support him with an allowance. The Capulets and Montagues have settled their feud. They petition the Prince to return Romeo to Verona, but Paris has influence at court and blocks any forgiveness of Romeo's crimes.

Meanwhile, the French have invaded, aided by Spanish mercenaries. Paris, a nobleman with political aspirations, has been off to war. Juliet and her daughter live at the Capulet home while Paris is away.

The child is to be baptized. The Friar gets word to Romeo. Romeo yearns to see the child. He returns to Verona incognito and attends the baptism disguised as the Friar's curate. Juliet is not there. Only Nurse with the child.
Romeo: Dear Nurse, It is I, Romeo.
Nurse: I am not your "Dear,' you useless boy! Go back to Mantua!
Romeo: Where is sweet Juliet? I long to see her.
Nurse: Juliet is not so sweet. She suffers horribly.
Romeo: How so, Dear Nurse?
Nurse: Come to the Capulet's garden tonight and see for yourself.
Romeo: And this beautiful child, does she fare well?
Nurse: She is the lucky one in this sad tale, hale and hearty despite the evil that swirls around her.
Romeo: That smile, those eyes, the point of the nose are as if I looked in a mirror!
Nurse: Think not those errant thoughts, boy! You have no standing in this city anymore. Your fantasies only make things worse.
Romeo: We will see tonight what standing I have.

The garden gate
Nurse: You will not know her by sight. She is sorely afflicted.
Romeo: By what foul spirit is she brought down.

Nurse: Her lord and master has brought the French disease into this house.

Romeo: There is no good in him. I should have killed him when I had the chance.

Nurse: What chance did you have? You a hot-headed boy and Paris a seasoned veteran of combat? You humor only yourself with your fantastic notions.

Romeo: Bring her to me, and we will see what future the present allows us.

Nurse exits and Juliet enters as Romeo paces. Her face is scarred from lesions. She wears a false nose. Her gait is unsteady and clearly painful.

Romeo: Is it you, the fair princess who rules my heart?

Juliet: There is nothing left of that girl. She is long gone.

Romeo: Sit with me and tell me there is hope for us.

Juliet: I did not wish to see you, but Nurse and Friar who have ministered to me in my travail persuaded me.

Romeo: I want you so! Our love is a torch in the darkness of our separation.

Juliet: Put out your torch. I am no more free than I was two years ago. Even less so. I am slave of man and sickness. You have a new life. Go back to it.

Romeo: There is no life without you. Paris is not here. You and the child can flee with me.

Juliet: It is true that he is off warring and whoring. But he has agents who watch me, and his return is imminent. I am a prisoner of his will.

Romeo: And what of the child? There is nothing of Paris about her. Surely she was conceived on the night we were truly married.

Juliet: I'll not say she's yours. Ever. I'll not put that idea in her head. You are merely someone I used to know. She is no business of yours. And I have not long to live. The pestilent worm is in my bones. Salves and baths and fumigations have no effect. I cry out until my family abandons their own home. I'm slipping into madness. I would end it all tonight, if I

115

could. If only the draught I drank that night in the crypt had truly been a poison.

Romeo: Your words are a knife in my heart. I came to rescue you, and all you want is death.

Juliet: There is no escape for me but death. It teases me, yet it comes not. Will you not at last do what is needed, and help me slip the bonds of earth?

Romeo: What you ask is murder!

Juliet: Is it not your duty, so far shirked, to make things right for the one you say you love?

Romeo: What future does our daughter have, if you are gone and Paris is ensconced in parenthood? Is she just another victim of his evil?

Juliet: Do what you must! Which guilt is harder to bear?

Two months later.

Romeo: I, Romeo, must fly, must sail away from this cursed land. I am never welcome in Verona again. My sins of omission and commission are too many.

Juliet is passed. A potion found its way to her lips, and her suffering is past.

Paris is dispatched. Not by my hand, alas. I wanted it so. He died, it is said, at the hand of his own troops, whom he abused without mercy.

The nurse, who says she will never forgive me for anything, yet won't leave the child with Juliet's parents, accompanies us.

The girl, Lucia, the child of what was once the world's greatest love, is with me. We embark for Hispaniola on a Spanish galleon, a cargo of sugar cane on board. Am I to be a farmer? There is danger, surely, in the New World, but also hope.

Fear and Loathing in a Suburban Strip Mall

OK, I had a few too many glasses of wine
at the Pinot and Pencils art party.
The situation wasn't helped by the fact
that I hadn't really wanted to go in the first place,
but my dog's psychiatrist said that my reclusiveness and
anxiety were making Trixie a nervous wreck,
so I should get out of the apartment and find some social
outlets for my emotional needs.
What did a dog psychiatrist know about my emotional
needs?

This episode coincided with a guy from my high school
class, who I hadn't seen in 30 freaking years,
popping up on Facebook Messenger.

He was back in town after a few decades on the West
Coast,
and why don't we get together, blah, blah, blah,
and I was about to send his missive to trash when he comes
across with this thing
about how he's invested in this Pinot and Pencils thing,
and they're opening in the upscale strip mall
where the old horse racing track used to be
this week, which is why he's back in town,
and he remembers how much I like art, blah,blah,blah,
and I think about Trixie chewing all the fur off her left front
leg,
so I say, "OK."

So let me just say here
that some guy you used to know in a generally vague kind
of way
in high school thirty years ago
trying to hook you up to spending fifty bucks
for a few glasses of grocery store grade California wine
and a packet of drawing pencils
is not a predictor of future success meeting your emotional
needs.
I mean, is this guy going to show me
and all the other middle age women in the room
which side of an orange to shade
to make it look round?
And is drawing an orange tonight going to raise my self-
esteem to the point
where I can go home and tell my neurotic dog to cut the
shit
and quit chewing on her leg or she's going back to the
pound?
And I could draw a perfectly good entire tree full of
oranges

thirty years ago in high school, so let's have another glass of Pinot
and get on to the Noir of self-portraiture.

So now I'm who knows how many sheets of velum and sticks of charcoal I'm into
let alone how many thin red lines of wine I've snorted,
and I'm looking in a mirror contemplating the essence of my being
and how to express that artistically,
and high school guy is there at my shoulder
looking at me looking at myself,
and he has this look on his face that's like
"Why didn't you go to prom with me?"
Like this was the sort of social outlet for my emotional needs in high school
that would have been good for me.
Like we could correct that deficit in my experience
later tonight.
Have some more wine.
And as he refills my glass with Chateau Doormat,
I notice that I am chewing on my left wrist
like a whacked out Yorkie
And this is what I have drawn...

Straitjacket Barbie

She had my lower lip captured between her teeth. If I pulled away, she bit down harder. I didn't want to pull away, but there is this automatic reaction, you know. I moved in and let our upper lips touch, she lightened up a bit. I was breathing short, rapid breaths. Her breath was slow and measured. She tasted like potato chips. Our noses were touching.

There were places on the playground. Shadows, corners, niches, crevices, shrubs and trees along the border. Teacher supervision was lax. You could sneak off and wedge yourself in where you wouldn't be seen. We were in second grade.

The sun was high in the sky. The air was hot and humid. We were frog squatting in the shade under the privet hedge next to the back entrance to the gymnasium. My legs were starting to cramp. I moved. She bit down. Maybe you think seven years old is a little young for this kind of thing to be going on. Maybe you don't spend a lot of time hanging around with kids. Maybe your supervision of your own kids is a little lax. Kids depend on lax supervision.

Her eyes were the brown of perfectly grilled waffles, sparkling with flecks of gold and orange. There was a trickle of blood in my mouth.

Something inside of me shifted that day.

She released me.

I asked her to marry me. She put a finger to my lips. She said, "Put some ice on that."

Barbie.

•

I don't remember everything. My memory is not working so well anymore. Episodes pop in and out like a TV series controlled by some mysterious outside force.

Sometimes I wish my mind would just leave me alone. The social worker says I should write it down then organize the bits. Organize Barbie! Good luck with that!

●

One day in third grade, I was leaning up against the wall near the back entrance to the gym. A bunch of kids were playing some kind of game of tag nearby. There was lots of laughing and screaming. I was uninterested. I hadn't seen Barbie in days. Barbie disappearing for extended periods of time disturbed me. Teachers and other kids acted like they hadn't noticed and didn't care. That disturbed me, too.

"Hey there, sad sack! You look like your best friend just died." Barbie smiled at me and punched me in the arm. "Don't worry. I'm back and better than ever."

She didn't look better than ever. She had the remnants of a black eye and a stitched-up, nasty looking cut on her cheekbone.

Kids get all sorts of bodily damage for all sorts of reasons...scrapes, bruises, etc. just from banging into stuff in the natural course of life. This wasn't like that.

"What happened to you?" I asked.

"Sometimes my parents and I have disagreements."

"That doesn't look like a disagreement." I frowned.

Yeah," she laughed, "sometimes we have these knockdown drag out family meetings."

"You mean they hit you?"

"Sometimes, but you should see them! Luckily we have the plastic surgeon who lives next door on retainer."

My mouth must have been hanging open. She closed it, politely, with her index finger, then touched my lips, then did the zipper gesture on her lips.

The bell for the end of recess rang. I walked with her back into the school. She was limping.

•

I never did really fully understand it, the thing with her and her parents. Her mom was always very nice to me. She gave me cookies and RC Cola, and she always smiled. Maybe I should have been suspicious of that. Her dad always called me James and shook my hand and gave me advice about the stock market, even though I was just a kid. Ok, that's bizarre.

But the thing with Barbie and her parents, it was intense. The wary way they looked at each other. The careful way they moved when they were all in the same room. The subtle undertones in their speech. I mean, whenever they were together, it was like everybody was hooked up to one of those lightning generators from the science museum and their hair was standing on end.

She told me they did stuff to her. Not just the fighting. Other stuff.

Ok, this is where you tell me that I should have reported this abuse to the proper authorities. Sure, but there was her finger on my lips and the look in her eyes that said, "Don't."

•

I had been vaguely aware of Barbie before that day in the bushes. I mean, there were a lot of kids in our school. Then there was the day she stole my cowboy hat. This was a real cowboy hat, not a toy. I had saved my allowance for months, and my mom had made a special trip downtown on the bus with me to get it.

Anyway, this girl swooped up from behind when I wasn't looking and snatched it off my head. Right in front of everybody. She ran off waving it over her head and whooping. Then she stopped and looked back at me. I chased her around the playground. She was very fast. Maybe I could have caught her. Maybe I could have wrestled the hat away from her. I didn't catch her. I didn't wrestle with her.

She put the hat in her cubby after recess. I guess I could have taken it at any point during the day. I didn't. There was something about her that I sensed in those moments of near contact. Maybe I wanted her to want something of mine. Maybe I wanted her to have it. I don't know. I was pretty young to be figuring out stuff like that. Anyway, I never did get my hat back.

●

Barbie's periods of disappearance got longer. Not like a vacation in the Bahamas. She would be hanging out with me at school one day, and the next day...no Barbie. It was fourth grade. Barbie had not come back from Christmas break. If I called the house, her mom would say, "Oh, hi, Jimmy. No she's not here. She's going to be out of town for a bit. Oh, sure, I'll have her call you when she gets back." Or her dad would answer the phone. "Good evening, James. Barbie? Didn't she tell you? Sorry. That girl is lax with her manners. She's visiting her maiden aunt in Poughkeepsie. Gotta run, son. And keep an eye on Imperial Oil." Click.

I knew Barbie pretty well at that point. We hung out together. We were best friends. Barbie didn't have an aunt in Poughkeepsie. What does a kid do with that? Maybe I should have called the authorities then. Maybe I should have told my parents. Maybe I should have done something. Anything. There were all these moments when action could have taken over from secrecy.

●

It was over a month later when she reappeared. I was leaning against the sun baked brick wall of the gym throwing rocks into the bushes. Barbie materialized out of nowhere and bit me on the neck.

I didn't even flinch. Just said, "Thanks for not saying goodbye and also thanks for not calling for months."

She said, "You're welcome and thanks for acting like it's OK to bite you on the neck instead of saying hello."

I couldn't help it. Being mad and lonely and scared all evaporated. "How's life in Poughkeepsie?"

She reached into her pocket and pulled out a strip of plastic. It had her name, Barbara Millicent Roberts, and her date of birth, and an ID number on it. A hospital wristband.

"Were you sick?"

"Not exactly."

"What do you mean 'not exactly'?"

"My parents put drugs in my food. The older I get, the harder it is for them to control me physically. I was kidnapped. I spent the last six months on a funny farm in upstate New York."

It didn't occur to me that she would make this stuff up. "We have to tell the police," I said. "My uncle works for the FBI."

"Jimmy, the police don't care. The school doesn't care. Nobody cares. They can do whatever they want to me, they are my parents, and there are doctors, and that is that."

"I care," I said.

She bit me on the other side of my neck and strolled lazily away. The cowboy hat, hanging by the stampede string bounced on her shoulders.

This was the worldview that Barbie was asking me to accept. If your parents are wealthy and influential and have friends who are wealthy and influential who will conspire with them, there is no other set of grownups who will help you. They can do whatever they want. My family wasn't like that. Why did Barbie have the power to sway me?

•

It is the year we are twelve. School is out. It is a blisteringly hot summer afternoon. It had been years since she last disappeared. I thought things were normalizing in the Roberts' house.

My parents think I am in the woods behind our house at the foot of The Ridge building a fort. I have walked for an hour to the top of The Ridge where Barbie lives.

The top of The Ridge is where the doctors and lawyers and banking executives live in large houses. Barbie's father is a banker. Her mother is a lawyer. Her parents are having cocktails with the plastic surgeon and his wife. Barbie is home alone. She is lounging by the pool. She is wearing a yellow seersucker jumper and her mother's sunglasses.

She says, "Jimmy, you're all hot and bothered. Get in the pool."

I just walked up here. I am hot and bothered. The pool looks great. I don't have swim trunks. She always had something daring to suggest. She was beyond interesting, more than exciting. Dangerous? Maybe.

"You don't need trunks to swim," she says. She takes me by the hand and leads me to the edge of the pool. I look away as she slides out of her clothes and into the water.

She laughs and swims to the deep end. She looks at me, not so much a dare as an I don't care. I take off my tennis shoes and my socks and my shirt. I take a deep breath. This is the moment I realize that the world does not leave you alone. I have to deal with it. I drop my shorts and underwear, I slip into the water.

"Why is your hair blonde?" I say.

Her hair is naturally brown, a little lighter than the irises of her eyes. She is tall for her age and skinny as a rail.

"My mother wants me to be blonde. 'I only have one life, so I should live it as a blonde.'" She mimics her mother's phony upper class intonation. " L'Oreal Paris Honey Blonde, to be exact."

She is a better swimmer than I am. She has a pool. We don't have pools at the foot of The Ridge. I am not one of the rich kids. My mom is a nurse and my dad inspects restaurants for the health department. I am mostly treading water. She glides like a dolphin, butts me with her head, pushes me with her feet, taunts me into trying to chase her. I might drown. I don't think she wants me to drown, but she does want me to chase her.

Later, we are sitting in the kitchen. She pops the tops on two fresh RC Colas. I ask her if she wants to live her life as a blonde. I say I liked her hair the way it was.

"I have to stop eating stuff my parents cook," she says. "I wake up two days later and my hair is a different color."

She gets the scissors from the junk drawer. She hands me the scissors and tells me to cut off her hair. I love her hair, even if it's the wrong color. I cut big chunks of hair from her head. "This is a good thing, Jimmy.," she says. Cut. Cut. I am cutting my lifeline to anonymity.

"Your mother will kill you." I say.

"Not kill," she says. "I'm too valuable an asset to kill." She takes the scissors and fake stabs at me. "Much worse than kill."

My mother hugs me when I walk in the door. I know she can smell the chlorine in my hair, but she asks, "How's the fort coming along?" This makes me want to cry, but I don't.

Two days later, I get an envelope in the mail. Inside is a Polaroid snap shot of Barbie with a fuzz of light hair on her head. The enclosed note says, "If I'm not dead, I'll see you later." A hand drawn heart split in two.

•

She has been gone for months. What year is it? Sometime in middle school. Barbie is back home. It is the end of the summer. We will be back in school in a few days. I have been granted an audience by her parents. "We always liked you, Jim," says her mother. "We are hoping you can be a good influence on Barbie. It is important for her to get along with others, to fit in."

I am pretty bent about this messed up situation and what it has done to Barbie. "Did you ever meet my Uncle Jack, Mrs. Roberts?"

"I don't think so, Jim. Where would we have met?"

"He works for the FBI. I thought maybe you would have crossed paths, being a lawyer. No? You're the kind of people he would like to know. Successful non-criminals. Change of pace from the scumbags he arrests every day. I'm thinking about a career with the FBI."

"That's lovely, Jim." She looks at me as if everything about her is completely normal. This is the moment when I think Barbie is wrong about all the other adults in the world.

Barbie is sitting in the den watching TV. I sit on the sofa next to her. She doesn't seem to recognize me. She stares at the TV. Her mother says, "I'll leave you two alone to catch up."

When her mother leaves the room, Barbie turns her head toward me while the rest of her body remains motionless. Just as I am about to be totally creeped out, she winks at me. I relax a little. She has the long blonde hair with a flip at the shoulder that her mother loves. Her eyes are a weird shade of blue now.

"How do they do that thing with your eyes?" I ask.

"Contact lenses." She pops one out. Now she has one brown eye and one blue eye, like a Huskie dog. I am now totally creeped out.

On the TV, there is a re-run of the documentary about the annual spaghetti harvest in Italy. Pasta hangs from the branches of trees. It is gathered by poor but hard working peasants.

"It's a spoof," she says. "Spaghetti doesn't grow on trees. Reality and fantasy. We need to know the difference."

Her mother comes back into the room with RC colas. Barbie goes semi-catatonic in her presence. Her mother smiles and leaves.

"Meet me on the old school playground at midnight," Barbie says. It's not far from her house, but it's a long hike for me, not that that's a deterrent.

"I'm supposed to be a good influence on you," I say.

"God, I hope not!" she says. Then she sips her RC and zones out on the spaghetti harvest.

We sit on the swings in the playground of our old elementary school, languidly moving like tired pendulums.

"It's a locked facility," she said.

"What are you talking about? A mental hospital?"

"We don't say 'mental' and we don't say 'hospital.' But there are doctors and nurses and aides and orderlies, and you can't leave if you want to."

"That's crazy! You're not crazy!" I started to swing more aggressively. "I think you're completely normal."

"We don't say 'crazy.' We say oppositional, and we say hyperactive, and we say possibly bipolar, and we say behavior modification, and we say give her some drugs so she is more cooperative in therapy."

"They drug you?"

"Sure, what else are they going to do?" She gets off the swing and grabs her backpack, digs around in it, and pulls out something white and floppy.

"Then there is our old friend, Mr. Straightjacket." She puts it on.

" Where did you get that?"

"I stole it."

"How do you steal a straightjacket from a…"

"Mental hospital? You'd be surprised what they don't see once you've calmed down and become more 'compliant.' Buckle up the back for me."

"No way."

"Don't worry. It's cool. Just be ready to be amazed."

I buckle it up and strap her arms down.

"Tighter," she says. "Imagine I am an unruly patient and you have to keep me from hitting you."

Really, I'm not into this at all. I step away. She lies down on the ground and curls up.

"OK, here we go," she says. "You have left the room. I am lying on my bed in a fetal position, all docile and quiet." She stands up. "While you were trying to strap me into the jacket, I was inflating my lungs and pressing outward with all my strength to increase the external volume of my torso. Now, I relax everything and shrink myself to acquire some wiggle room. Luckily, I am thin enough, and I have a loose shoulder joint from a previous incident that never healed up right, so I can now get my arms over my head and then get the arm buckles to the front and unlatch them with my teeth. Now I can just slough off the jacket." She tosses it to the ground. "Voila! Houdini is alive inside all of us!"

"Holy crap!"

"Yeah, neat trick. But the doors are still locked. The most important thing is to learn how they want you to be, then be that way when you're not drugged up. They get tired of you pretty quickly, if you're subdued all the time, so they send you home, and your parents like it, if you're subdued all the time, so you get to stay home. I was so stupid. Took me years to figure out how to pass."

I hand her the jacket, but she says, "No. You keep it."

"What am I going to do with a straightjacket? If my parents find it, there'll be a whole lot of explaining to do, and I don't want to have to explain this."

"You're a clever boy," she said. She kissed me on the forehead and headed for home.

"Forehead kiss. Nice!" I shouted after her.

•

Barbie hasn't gone MIA for a long time. Things at her house are still tense but seemingly non-violent. A truce, but no one surrendering yet.

We are in high school. Sophomoric. Barbie has made it through almost the entire year. Her parents bought her a car in recognition of her compliance. She picks me up at my house and drives me over the Ridge to our school, Carnegie Prep. Pink Mustang convertible. Un...believable.

I ask her if she is done fighting with her parents.

"I can, but I won't," she says, "as long as they leave me alone. I now have a very fulfilling inner life."

.

Barbie says she doesn't want to have sex or get married or have kids. Her parents want her dating rich kids and marrying money. Making key alliances through marriage.

Her parents are now controlling how she dresses...makeup, jewelry, perfume. Hairstyles. Blond hair and blue eyes. Posture. Social niceties and etiquette. Going to the country club. Debutantes. Dances. Golf. Sailing. Tennis. Food choices. Politics. Making her into Barbie Dream Date. All this takes up a lot of her time. I don't get to see her as much as I would like. Then I realize she is gone. It's been weeks. I thought we were past that.

I call my uncle. He has been discreetly checking on a few things.

.

It's Thursday night. Mr. & Mrs. Roberts are out of the house. It's bridge night with the plastic surgeon and his wife. They will be playing cards and drinking cocktails until midnight.

I sneak out of my bedroom and scale the Ridge to Barbie's house. They haven't paid the security company for months, and I know the latch on the patio door is weak. I am easily inside and make my way to the office. I find the files and make copies. I stop for a moment and look into Barbie's bedroom. Hanging on her mirror is my cowboy hat. I almost take it with me, but no. Heavy sigh. I am out and back home before eleven.

.

"If you are sixteen," Barbie says, "and you are tall and slim, some people, like my idiot parents, might think you are less than attractive to the opposite sex."

We are sitting by the pool. I came over after school. It's late spring, and it's been a hot day, so the water is tolerable.

"I always found you attractive," I say.

"You don't have any money, Jimmy, or my parents would be all over you."

"I have two shares of Imperial Oil. Imperial Oil is doing very well."

She smiles. She stands up, takes off her black and white striped swimsuit and dives into the pool. She floats on her back. "What am I going to do with these boobs? It's like having a pair of basketballs strapped to my chest." She flips over. "And this ass. Who has an ass like this?"

I shake my head. How ridiculously absurd is this body modification her parents have imposed on her!

She gets out of the pool and starts walking toward the house. "I'm getting the scissors," she says. "You call 911."

I grab her arm. "No way. Not necessary. There are things in play. Be patient."

She stops and looks at me. "Jimmy, what have you done?"

Ken Carson. He's a junior. Captain of the lacrosse team. His father is ambassador to Switzerland. His mother is president of the Junior League. They are the richest people in our town. It is known about Ken's parents that they dote on him, and what makes him happy makes them happy, and money is no object. It is known about Ken that he likes girls with blonde hair and blue eyes and big boobs and round asses. This is all going to work out for Barbie's parents, because the new and improved Barbie is Ken's prom date. It is kismet.

Barbie has returned my cowboy hat in exchange for the straightjacket.

I have the keys to the Mustang. I just have a learner's permit. I can't legally drive this car. Sometimes you have to break some eggs, even if an omelette may not be the outcome.

After the prom, Barbie will have Ken take her to the old grade school playground. He will think he's getting laid. I will show up in the nick of time to rescue the princess.

When I get there, Ken is in the straightjacket. It is not commonly known that Ken is a little kinky. His pants are around his ankles. I was not expecting this.

Barbie is sitting on one of the swings, smoking a cigarette. "This has been great for me, Ken. How was it for you?"

Ken is yelling obscenities.

"Shut up, Ken," Barbie says. "There could be pictures." She has her trusty Polaroid. "Would you like there to be pictures?"

Ken shakes his head.

"Oops! My finger slipped!" The Polaroid spit out an embarrassing full frontal.

"Would you like to go to school somewhere far, far away, Ken?"

"Fuck, you Barbie!" says Ken.

The Polaroid whirs and spits out another photo.

"Maybe in Switzerland, mein Herr?"

"Fine. Just get me out of this thing and let me go home."

Barbie hands me the camera and the candid shots and unbuckles the straightjacket. Ken pulls up his pants and runs.

"Home, Jeeves!" Barbie says.

Back at Barbie's house. Crime scene tape. Vehicles with flashing lights. People in FBI jackets are carrying boxes of documents to waiting vehicles.

"Jesus on crutches!" Barbie says.

My Uncle Jack was very interested in the secret life of her parents. Barbie's dad had not been employed at the bank for the last several years. They had been living on a combination of insider trading, conspiracy, a Ponzi scheme, wire fraud, tax evasion. Old George and Margaret Roberts have a lot of explaining to do. A similar scenario was being played out at the home of the plastic surgeon.

"What happens to me, now?" Barbie asked.

"There's a guest room at my house," I said. "Your parents will be tied up for a considerable time. You're sixteen. You can apply to be emancipated by the courts. My parents have some friends in the actually legitimate medical community who will help you get your body back."

•

Maybe I should have figured out how to intervene sooner. Barbie went through hell, and she was supposedly the most important person in my life. But I didn't. When things were less crazy, I thought everything would be OK. Then another thing would happen. Worse than the one before, and I would think I should have done something, but I didn't. Finally, I found the wherewithal to do something. Was it too late? Was Barbie scarred for life?

What does a kid know? How can a kid make adults stop doing horrible things? How can anybody make the world make sense?

Where did Barbie go when the court declared her to be responsible for herself? Where is my cowboy hat?

The social worker has gone home. She says it's good for me to tell my story, write it down. She smiles as if she is indulging the fantasies of a senile old man.

133

It's late at night. Sometimes I am a docile and compliant resident of this fine facility, sometimes not so much. The staff are drinking coffee in the lounge and gossiping. They won't check on me until morning.

I am on the floor curled up in a fetal position trying to get my shoulder to dislocate, so I can get out of this damn straightjacket.

ABOUT THE AUTHOR

David H. Reinarz has been writing fiction short stories and poetry since October 2015. He participated in the 7 Doctors Writers Workshop sponsored by the University of Nebraska Medical Center in Omaha and by The Nebraska Writers Collective. He continues to participate in a 7 Doctors Alumni Group.

Dave lives in Omaha with the love of his life, Lynne.

Dave was born in Minneapolis, MN. A significant part of his childhood was spent in Chattanooga, TN. His family moved to Omaha when he was 15. He graduated from Benson High School. He attended the University of Nebraska at Omaha and graduated with a BA in Philosophy and Religious Studies. He is retired from a thirty year career of managing professional retail bicycle shops.

Contact information:

dhr.author@gmail.com

Facebook: David H. Reinarz, Author